WORLD OF SPORT QUIZ BOOK

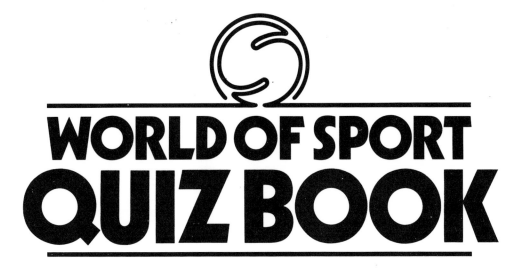

WORLD OF SPORT
QUIZ BOOK

INTRODUCED BY
DICKIE DAVIES

STANLEY PAUL
London Melbourne Sydney Auckland Johannesburg

Stanley Paul & Co. Ltd

An imprint of the Hutchinson Publishing Group

17–21 Conway Street, London W1P 6JD

Hutchinson Group (Australia) Pty Ltd
30–32 Cremorne Street, Richmond South, Victoria 3121
PO Box 151, Broadway, New South Wales 2007

Hutchinson Group (NZ) Ltd
32–34 View Road, PO Box 40-086, Glenfield, Auckland 10

Hutchinson Group (SA) Pty Ltd
PO Box 337, Bergvlei 2012, South Africa

First published 1982
© London Weekend Television 1982

Photoset by Rowland Phototypesetting Ltd,
Bury St Edmunds, Suffolk
Printed in Great Britain by St Edmundsbury Press,
Bury St Edmunds, Suffolk, and bound by
Wm Brendon & Son Ltd, Tiptree, Essex

British Library Cataloguing in Publication Data
World of Sport quiz book.
  1. Sports – Miscellanea
  I. Davies, Dickie
  796'.076   GV706.8

ISBN 0 09 149901 1

ACKNOWLEDGEMENTS

For permission to reproduce copyright photographs, the publishers would like to thank Russ Adams, Allsport, Colorsport, Patrick Eagar, Robin Eley Jones, Keystone, E.D. Lacey, Leo Mason, Morley L. Pecker, Press Association, Schirner, Syndication International and Steve Yarnell

DICKIE DAVIES WRITES...

Hello there! I'm very happy to be able to introduce to you this new venture by 'World of Sport'.

Sports facts – records, personal biographical details, off-beat happenings, statistics – seem to have almost as much fascination for sports fans as events do themselves.

At 'World of Sport' we are assisted by various experts, but from time to time we have to admit to a minor slip-up. It's then that we realize just how well-informed our viewers really are, because we're invariably told about it by phone while the show is still on the air. And when we set competition problems on the air, not only is the postcard response astonishingly high, but also the percentage of correct answers.

Furthermore, we regularly get letters from viewers asking us to help clear up disagreements which have arisen in pubs and elsewhere about matters of fact. We do what we can, since we always like to keep the peace!

So we know that, among our viewers, we have a large number of sports experts who enjoy pitting their wits against us, as well as against each other. One of these, for instance, is my colleague from 'Weekend World', Brian Walden, who reels out past Cup Final teams like a fisherman on to a salmon. And you'd be pressed to trick the bar staff here at our South Bank studios – they've often managed to get even our research team guessing.

We are sure that this book will intrigue, stimulate and entertain you. The questions cover a wide range of sports, some of which are not often seen on our programme, but go to make up the whole pattern of sport. They vary in difficulty, so there should be something in this book for everyone.

Let's get the ball rolling with one from me. Which World Heavyweight Champion appeared in a play based on a novel by George Bernard Shaw at Daly's Theater, New York? Answer: 'Gentleman' Jim Corbett in *Cashel Byron's Profession*. I must admit I only found that out today!

Good quizzing.

QUESTIONS

ASSOCIATION FOOTBALL

A MIXED BAG

1 Which League club is nicknamed The Pilgrims?
2 Who in 1956, became the first goalkeeper to win the Footballer of the Year Award?
3 Who played for England during the 1962 World Cup whilst he was playing League football in Italy for Inter Milan?
4 Name the only country not to lose a match during the final stages of the 1974 World Cup?
5 Who managed England in between Alf Ramsey and Don Revie as caretaker manager?
6 Who is the current Secretary of the Football Association?
7 Who were the first winners of the FA Cup?
8 Arsenal and which other team has won the First Division title three years in succession?
9 Who did Dixie Dean score his 60th League goal against in the 1927–28 season to establish a new goal-scoring record?
10 Which club did Tony Woodcock join in 1979 upon leaving Nottingham Forest?
11 Who was England's leading goal-scorer in the 1954 World Cup?
12 Which club, in having a player sent off in 1971, had their first player dismissed for 31 years?
13 Stanford was the second christian name of which member of the England World Cup winning team in 1966?
14 Tottenham Hotspur, the holders, were eliminated in the first round of the Cup Winners' Cup in 1963–64 – by whom?
15 Who was Bill Shankly's last signing for Liverpool before his retirement?
16 Which was Gordon Lee's first club as a manager?
17 George Best was sent off in the second leg of Manchester United's World Club championship game against Estudiantes in 1968, but which United player was sent off in the first leg?
18 Who was the goalkeeper poised for a move to Manchester United in 1978 for a record £440,000, but the deal was halted due to adverse medical reports on him?
19 Who was the England player sent off in the 1977 international against Argentina?
20 The first full international to be played entirely under floodlights in Britain was at Wembley in 1963 when England beat which team 8–3?
21 Who was the first Czechoslovakian player to win the European Footballer of the Year Award?
22 Which was the first team after the last war to be beaten in three FA Cup Finals?
23 Which man played against Real Madrid in the very first European Cup Final, and then later played for Madrid in several other finals?
24 Who, in 1970, became the first player to score a goal in every round of the World Cup?
25 Who is the only Bristol Rovers player to have played for England in a full international?

WHICH COUNTRY?

The following players all appeared in the 1966 World Cup Finals in England. You have to marry them up with the country they played for.

1 Mazurkiewicz	(a) W. Germany
2 Hottges	(b) Italy
3 Carbajal	(c) USSR
4 Iribar	(d) Mexico
5 Manga	(e) Uruguay
6 Jose Perreira	(f) Spain
7 Li Chan Myung	(g) Argentine
8 Albertosi	(h) Brazil
9 Roma	(i) North Korea
10 Yachin	(j) Portugal

PICTURE QUIZ 1

After Poland had knocked England out of the 1974 World Cup, this squad was picked to represent England in their next international game. Name the squad.

THE 500 CLUB

Listed below are details of 10 well-known Football League players, all of whom have made over 500 Football League appearances. Their first and last clubs are given, together with the years they played in the Football League and their total number of appearances. You have to identify them.

	First club	Last club	Years played	No. of Appearances
1	Swindon Town	Stockport County	1959–79	713
2	Portsmouth	Wolves	1957–74	532
3	Barnsley	Tottenham H	1948–63	553
4	West Ham	West Brom	1959–75	522
5	Halifax	Chesterfield	1958–73	563
6	Sunderland	Middlesbrough	1952–66	504
7	Newcastle Utd	Stoke City	1956–74	515
8	Northwich Vics	Manchester City	1894–1924	670
9	Leicester City	QPR	1959–76	607
10	Chesterfield	Stoke City	1958–72	510

PICTURE QUIZ 2

1 Name the players.
2 And the year.
3 Who was the first PFA player of the year?

4 Who was the first PFA young player of the year?
5 Who won both awards (PFA player and young player) in 1977?

NEW TO THE LEAGUE

The following are all questions about clubs that have joined the Football League.

1 Who replaced Bradford Park Avenue in the Football League?
2 The league was extended to 92 clubs in 1950–51 as a result of four clubs joining the League. Name any two of the four.

3 Which was the last club before Wigan Athletic to join the Football League?
4 Which team replaced Gateshead in the Football League?
5 They left the League in 1931, but were elected back two years later. Name them.
6 Which current First Division team only joined the Football League as recently as 1938?

SO YOU THINK YOU KNOW THE FA CUP?

1 Who, in the 1977–78 season, became only the second player to be sent off in an FA Cup semifinal?
2 Who was Manchester City's goalkeeper when they won the FA Cup in 1969?
3 Who captained Aston Villa when they last won the FA Cup in 1957?
4 Who was the player who appeared in the FA Cup Finals of 1951, 1953 and 1958?
5 Which is the only club to have been beaten in two successive FA Cup Finals at Wembley?
6 Who was the player who opened the scoring in the 1959 FA Cup Final and was later carried off with a broken leg?
7 Who scored Southampton's goal in the 1976 Final?
8 Which was the first club in the twentieth century to win the FA Cup two years in succession?
9 Who scored goals in the FA Cup Finals of 1953 and 1958?
10 Which was the first Yorkshire team to win the FA Cup?

A MIXED BAG FOR THE EXPERT

1 Only three men have played at Wembley whilst over the age of 40: Stanley Matthews and John Oakes of Charlton Athletic are two. The third man played for Hillingdon in the 1971 FA Challenge Trophy final against Telford. Name him.
2 Who played his 100th game for Brazil against England in 1969?
3 Only two clubs have spent each one of the League's 82 years in the top two divisions. Everton is one. Name the other.

ASSOCIATION FOOTBALL

4 Which club has played in the First Division of the Football League, the Third Division, the Fourth Division, but not the Second Division?
5 Who was the member of the England World Cup squad of 1962 who was also assistant manager to Walter Winterbottom at the time?
6 Who was the Scotsman who took charge of the England Under-23 team that toured Hungary, Turkey and Israel in 1964?
7 Which club conceded three own goals against Wolves in the 1971–72 UEFA Cup?
8 If you were watching the 'Strongest' playing 'Always Ready' in a League match, which country would you be in?
9 Which is the only side to be relegated from the First Division and play in one of the three major European competitions in the same season?
10 Which player was sent off for Burnley against Blackpool on Boxing Day 1972, on his Football League debut?
11 Leeds United, Liverpool, Manchester United, Wolves, and which other team, have all won the FA Cup and been runners-up in the First Division the same season, since the war?
12 Which man, in only his second full game for Norwich City, appeared for them in the 1973 League Cup Final at Wembley?
13 Who played in two postwar FA Cup Finals before he was 21, and was on the losing side each time?
14 Three non-League sides have reached the fifth round of the FA Cup since the war. Yeovil Town and Blyth Spartans are two. Name the third.
15 Who was the English referee in charge of the violent World Cup game in 1962 when Italy played Chile?

PICTURE QUIZ 3

It's not necessary to name the dogs – the players are perhaps more difficult. One is a West Ham player, another is the West German left wing in the 1966 World Cup final. And you don't get any extra marks for naming the goalkeeper.

IN WHAT YEAR?

Listed below are three clues that will reveal the year in which various footballing events took place. You have to identify them.

1 *Clue 1*: Republic of Ireland beat England 2–0 at Goodison Park.
Clue 2: Italian team Torino tragically wiped out in plane crash.
Clue 3: Johnny Carey elected Footballer of the Year.

2 *Clue 1*: First European Cup Final between Real Madrid and Rheims is played.
Clue 2: Chelsea are First Division Champions for the first and only time.
Clue 3: Former England captain Ron Flowers made his international debut.

3 *Clue 1*: First £500,000 transfer between two Football League clubs.
Clue 2: Tommy Docherty takes charge of Queen's Park Rangers for second time.
Clue 3: Nottingham Forest retain Football League Cup.

4 *Clue 1*: Leeds United become the first British club to win the Fairs Cup.
Clue 2: Matt Busby is knighted.
Clue 3: Pietro Anastasi signed by Juventus for a £440,000 world record fee.

5 *Clue 1*: Jimmy Dickinson becomes the first player to make 700 League appearances.
Clue 2: Denis Law is the European Footballer of the Year.
Clue 3: Leeds United and Sunderland are promoted to First Division.

PICTURE QUIZ 4

1 Name the teams.
2 Name the ground.
3 Who is the PFA administrator in the picture?

GROUNDS AND NICKNAMES

The grounds and nicknames of ten Football League clubs are listed below, but they are all mixed up. You have to sort them out so that each club is given its correct ground and nickname.

Club		Nickname		Ground
Bury	**1**	The Shrimpers	(a)	Boundary Park
Oldham Athletic	**2**	The Lions	(b)	Vetch Field
Rotherham United	**3**	The Shakers	(c)	Sincil Bank
Southend United	**4**	The Imps	(d)	Goodison Park
Everton	**5**	The Hatters	(e)	Griffin Park
Brentford	**6**	The Latics	(f)	Roots Hall
Luton Town	**7**	The Bees	(g)	The Den
Lincoln City	**8**	The Swans	(h)	Millmoor
Swansea City	**9**	The Merry Millers	(i)	Kenilworth Road
Millwall	**10**	The Toffees	(j)	Gigg Lane

NAME THE CLUBS

	Year formed	Highest ever League position	FA Cup wins	Record attendance	Three postwar managers
1	1887	Div. 2 (3rd)	1	40,255	Tim Ward, Jim Iley, Johnny Steele
2	1863	Div. 1 (4th)	0	51,380	Frank Taylor, Alan A'Court, Bob McGrory
3	1884	Div. 1 Champions	1	41,826	Harry Storer, Tim Ward, Dave McKay
4	1885	Div. 1 (4th)	2	35,000	Bob Stokoe, Les Shannon, Tommy McAnearney
5	1894	Div. 1 (2nd)	0	43,335	Peter Doherty, Fred Ford, Pat Beasley

FILL IN THE BLANKS

Complete the missing details on the list of
European Cup Finals below:

Year	Winners		Runners-up		Venue
1956	Real Madrid	4	Rheims	(a)	Paris
1957	Real Madrid	2	AC Fiorentina	0	Madrid
1958	Real Madrid	3	AC Milan	2	Brussels
1959	Real Madrid	2	Rheims	0	Stuttgart
1960	Real Madrid	7	Eintracht Frankfurt	3	(b)
1961	Benfica	3	Barcelona	2	Berne
1962	Benfica	(c)	Real Madrid	3	Amsterdam
1963	AC Milan	2	(d)	1	London
1964	Inter Milan	3	Real Madrid	1	Vienna
1965	Inter Milan	1	Benfica	0	(e)
1966	Real Madrid	(f)	Partizan Belgrade	1	Brussels
1967	Celtic	2	Inter Milan	1	Lisbon
1968	Manchester United	4	Benfica	1	London
1969	AC Milan	4	Ajax	1	Madrid
1970	Feyenoord	2	Celtic	1	Milan
1971	Ajax	2	(g)	0	London
1972	Ajax	2	Inter Milan	0	Rotterdam
1973	Ajax	1	Juventus	0	Belgrade
1974	Bayern Munich (after 1–1 draw)	4	Atletico Madrid	0	Brussels
1975	Bayern Munich	2	Leeds United	(h)	Paris
1976	Bayern Munich	1	(i)	0	Glasgow
1977	Liverpool	3	Borussia Mönchen Gladbach	1	(j)
1978	Liverpool	1	FC Bruges	0	London
1979	Nottm Forest	1	Malmo	0	Munich
1980	Nottm Forest	1	SV Hamburg	0	Madrid
1981	Liverpool	1	Real Madrid	0	Paris

Name the course and the Football League ground.

FORWARD LINES

Listed below are the forward lines of postwar FA Cup Final teams. You have to give the team concerned, and the year they appeared in the final.

1 Fern; Gibson; Lochhead; Clarke; Glover
2 Bimpson; Dobing; Dougan; Douglas; MacLeod
3 Giles; Storey; Peacock; Collins; Johannson
4 Wilson; Ashworth; Dawson; Spavin; Holden
5 Payne; Baron; Stubbins; Fagan; Liddell
6 Gilchrist; Channon; Osgood; McCalliog; Stokes
7 Pugh; Fantham; McCalliog; Ford; Quinn
8 Bingham; Brown; Morton; Cummins; Gregory

ASSOCIATION FOOTBALL

THE WORLD CUP

1 When Juste Fontaine set up a World Cup scoring record with 13 goals in the 1958 tournament, whose record did he beat?

2 In their group games in the 1966 World Cup North Korea beat Italy, lost to USSR and drew with which country?

3 Who was the last man before Eusebio to score four goals in a World Cup match?

4 Who scored four goals in a World Cup match yet finished up on the losing side?

5 Which team was eliminated in the quarter-final stages of the World Cup despite the fact that they scored five goals?

6 Which team beat Scotland 7–0 in the 1954 tournament?

7 Which team did Pele score his first World Cup goal against (in final stages of tournament)?

8 Which was the last country to reach the final of the World Cup and not take part in the next competition before Holland in 1982?

9 El Salvador reached the final stages of the 1970 World Cup but one of their qualifying matches led to a three-day war between the two countries. Who were their opponents?

10 Two of the players who appeared for England in the 1966 World Cup Final did not play in the opening match of the series against Uruguay. Name them.

11 Which is the only country Wales have beaten in the final stages of the World Cup?

12 Who was manager of the Italian team that won the World Cup in 1934 and 1938?

13 Who was the Briton who refereed the final match of the 1950 World Cup between Uruguay and Brazil?

14 Two Germans played in the four consecutive World Cup tournaments from 1958 to 1970. Name either.

15 Name the three European countries to have appeared in the very first World Cup Final in 1930, and also the last one, in 1982?

PICTURE QUIZ 6

1 Who is this ITV commentator?

2 Why was he photographed like this?

3 On which ground was this photo taken?

ATHLETICS

WHOM DID THEY SUCCEED?

Below is a list of postwar world record-holders, and the date they set their world records. You have to state who held the world record immediately prior to them.

Record holder	Event	Year set
1 Sebastian Coe	800 metres	1979
2 Filbert Bayi	1500 metres	1974
3 Sebastian Coe	Mile	1979
4 Henry Rono	3000 metres	1978
5 Kip Keino	5000 metres	1965
6 David Bedford	10000 metres	1973
7 Ed Moses	400 metres hurdles	1976
8 Valeriy Brumel	High jump	1961
9 Ralph Boston	Long jump	1960
10 Kjell Isaksson	Pole vault	1972

WHAT NATIONALITY?

Give the nationalities of the following ten postwar Olympic champions:

Winner	Event	Year(s)
1 J. Bartel	Men's 1500 metres	1952
2 M. Nemeth	Men's Javelin	1976
3 J. Akii Bua	Men's 400 metres hurdles	1972
4 I. Balas	Women's high jump	1960/64
5 W. Komar	Men's shot	1972
6 G. E. G. Reiff	Men's 5000 metres	1948
7 J. Winter	Men's high jump	1948
8 B. Schul	Men's 5000 metres	1964
9 Y. Williams	Women's long jump	1952
10 D. Cabrera	Marathon	1948

WHO AM I?

Identify each of the following three famous athletes from the clues given:

1 *Clue 1*: Born in 1951 of a Polish father and Scottish mother.
Clue 2: At 1976 Olympics he smashed the world record in the steeplechase but only ended up winning the silver medal.
Clue 3: He won his elusive Olympic gold medal in 1980, only to lose his life in a car accident 12 months later.

2 *Clue 1*: Born in 1958 of a Nigerian father and a Scottish mother, with the christian names of Francis Morgan.
Clue 2: He set a world record in May 1980 only to lose it less than a month later to Guido Kratchmer.
Clue 3: One of Britain's four gold medallists at the 1980 Moscow Olympics.

3 *Clue 1*: Born in Oslo in 1953 an outstanding middle/long-distance runner of the 1970s and 1980s.
Clue 2: She went to the 1976 Olympics as world 1500 metres record-holder, but failed to reach the final.
Clue 3: She completed a hat trick of world cross-country title wins in 1980.

OLYMPIC VENUES

1 Which city staged the very first Olympics in 1896?
2 Which city will stage the next summer Olympics – in 1984?
3 Which was the last city to stage the Olympics that did not begin with the letter M?
4 Which was the last European city before Moscow to stage the summer Olympics?
5 In what year were the last Olympic Games to be staged in Great Britain?
6 Which city staged the 1980 Winter Olympics?

ATHLETICS

FOR THE EXPERT

1 Who was the only Briton to take part in the men's 100 metres at the 1976 Montreal Olympics?
2 Who in 1977, was the last man to defeat Steve Ovett in a mile race before Sydney Marree in 1981?
3 Which woman won four gold medals in the European Championships between 1966 and 1974?
4 Wolverhampton and Bilston were British League Division One champions for 1975, 1976 and 1977. Which club were the champions in the three years prior to this?
5 Tony Satchwell finished seventh in both the shot and the discus at the 1974 Commonwealth Games. Which country did he represent?
6 Only four athletes took part in both the 1966 Commonwealth Games and the 1978 Games. One was British. Name him or her.
7 Who was the only double individual medallist at the 1976 Olympics, apart from Ivo Van Damme, not to have won a gold medal?
8 Who was the last man to hold the world 800-metres record and world mile record simultaneously prior to Sebastian Coe?
9 Who set up a Commonwealth Games long jump record at 25 feet 4 inches at the 1962 Games yet only finished fourth?
10 Christine Benning of Britain set a United Kingdom all-comers' record in the 1500 metres in 1978. What was her maiden name?
11 England were first and second in the men's shot at the 1974 Commonwealth Games. Geoff Capes won the gold. Who won the silver?
12 Britain had two finalists in the men's 1500 metres at the Montreal Olympics. David Moorcroft was one. Name the other.

PICTURE QUIZ 1

An unusual photo of a well-known athlete – why?

WHO WAS THE FIRST?

Who was the first . . .

1 . . . woman to run a mile in under five minutes?
2 . . . man to jump 7 feet in the high jump?
3 . . . woman to jump 6 feet in the high jump?
4 . . . man to run 200 metres in under 20 seconds?
5 . . . man to run a mile in under 3 minutes 55 seconds?
6 . . . man to run 10,000 metres in under 28 minutes?
7 . . . man to jump over 28 feet in the long jump?
8 . . . man to put the shot over 70 feet?
9 . . . woman to jump over 22 feet in the long jump?
10 . . . woman to put the shot over 60 feet?

PICTURE QUIZ 2

1 Who are they?
2 Which countries do they represent?
3 At which Olympics did the athlete on his back win gold medals?
4 To whom did the athlete in the flowery shirt lose his world record?
5 How many Olympic golds did K2 win?
6 What world record did K1 hold?
7 In which country is no. 911 now living?
8 Which of the athletes have won Olympic steeplechase medals?

ATHLETICS

WORLD MILE RECORD

1 Since the world mile record went under four minutes, which man has held the record for the longest period?
2 When Bannister became the first man to run the mile in under four minutes, whose record of 4 minutes 1.4 seconds did he beat – a record that had stood for the previous nine years?
3 Who was the last Briton before Sebastian Coe in 1979 to hold the world mile record?
4 Since the world record dropped below four minutes, who has held the record for the shortest period?
5 Who set a postwar world mile record in Dublin?
6 When Sebastian Coe and Steve Ovett broke the world mile record for the first time, both did so in the same stadium – which?
7 Who was the last Briton before Roger Bannister to hold the world mile record?
8 Who was the first man to take the world record under 3 minutes 50 seconds?
9 Only two men have broken their own world mile record since the war: Jim Ryun – and who else?
10 Who finished second to Bannister when he became the first man to run a sub-four-minute mile, and also second to Landy when he became the second man to do so?

A MIXED BAG

1 Which man won fourteen AAA sprint titles between 1946 and 1953?
2 Who was the French girl who beat Lillian Board into second place in the 400 metres final at the 1964 Olympics?
3 Who was the first man to run a mile in exactly four minutes?
4 Who was the athlete who lit the flame at the 1956 Melbourne Olympics and later went on to break world records in eight different events?
5 Who was the first athlete to win a triple set of gold medals by winning the Olympics, the European Championships, and the Commonwealth Games titles?
6 Which is the only event contested by both men and women at the Olympics that the United States have not won since the war?
7 In which country was British runner David Jenkins born?
8 Which Briton won the hammer at the Commonwealth Games in 1962, 1966 and 1970?
9 Which runner, along with Tommie Smith, performed the Black Power demonstration during the 200 metres medal ceremony at the 1968 Olympics?
10 What is traditionally the last event of the decathlon?
11 Wilma Rudolph won the gold medals in both the ladies' 100 and 200 metres at the 1960 Rome Olympics. Which other girl won medals in both these events?
12 Who were the husband and wife who won individual gold medals at the 1952 Helsinki Olympics?

THE MARATHONS

1 Who is the only man since the war to have retained his Olympic marathon title?
2 Who was the Cuban, now a naturalized American, who won the 1980 New York City Marathon?
3 Who won the 1981 Boston Marathon?
4 Which Briton finished third in the New York City Marathon in both 1976 and 1977?
5 Who was the first woman home in the 1981 London Marathon?
6 Name either of the two men who came home joint first in the inaugural London Marathon in 1981?

IN WHICH EVENT?

In which event have the following been postwar Olympic gold medallists?

1 Peter Snell; Ralph Doubell; Dave Wottle
2 Bob Beamon; Ralph Boston; Randy Williams
3 David Hemery; Ed Moses; Glenn Davis
4 Jim Hines; Haseley Crawford; Allan Wells
5 Mac Wilkins; Al Oerter; Ludvik Danek
6 Dick Fosbury; Charles Dumas; Valeriy Brumel
7 Herb Elliott; Peter Snell; Kip Keino
8 Valeriy Borzov; Don Quarrie; Pietro Mennea
9 Udo Beyer; Randy Matson; Parry O'Brien
10 Murray Halberg; Vladimir Kuts; Emil Zatopek

RULE BRITANNIA

1 Who was the first Welshman to win an Olympic gold medal?
2 Who was the Briton who came second to Vladimir Kuts in the 1956 5000-metres final?
3 Who was the British girl who won the silver medal in the long jump behind Viscopoleanu at the 1968 Olympics?
4 Which Briton finished second in the 50 kilometre walk at the 1964 Olympics behind winner Pamich?
5 Who is the only Briton to have won the men's 100 metres at the Olympics other than Allan Wells?
6 Mary Rand won the first ever British gold medal in the ladies' events at the Olympic Games. Who won the second?
7 Who was the Briton who won a silver medal in the 3000-metres steeplechase at the 1964 Olympics?
8 Pascoe, Hemery and Jenkins were three of the squad that won the silver medal in the 4 x 400 metres relay at the 1972 Munich Games. Name the fourth member of the squad.
9 Iolande Balas won the gold medal in the ladies' high jump at the 1960 Olympics. Two girls tied for second place – one was British. Name her.
10 Who was the Briton who won the gold medal in the 20-kilometres walk at the 1964 Games?

BADMINTON

1 What is the height to the centre of the net in a game of badminton?
2 The Thomas Cup is awarded in the Men's International Team Championships. What is the name of the trophy that the women contest?
3 Who was the English girl who won the All-England Championship in 1978?
4 Who was the Indonesian player who won the All-England Championship every year from 1968 to 1974 inclusive?
5 Who was the Dane who won the men's singles title at the European Championships for the third successive year in 1980?
6 What nationality is World Ladies' Champion Lene Köppen?
7 Which country has won the Thomas Cup on the most number of occasions?
8 What is the overall length of a badminton court?
9 How many feathers are there on a standard shuttlecock?
10 Who are the only Britons to have won world titles?

PICTURE QUIZ

Who is this international, pictured at the age of eighteen?

BIATHLON

1 Which country has provided the greatest number of biathlon world champions?
2 The biathlon was first introduced into the winter Olympics at Squaw Valley. In what year?
3 Over what distance is a competitive biathlon run?
4 When firing the rifle, are the competitors in the standing or the prone position?
5 How many runners are there per team in an Olympic biathlon relay?
6 If a contestant fails to hit one of the targets in a relay race, what must he do?
7 Which country has won all four biathlon team relays at the Olympics?
8 What nationality was Adolf Wiklund, the first world champion?
9 What is the difference in the shooting section between a relay biathlon and an individual biathlon?

BILLIARDS

1 How many points are awarded for a cannon?
2 What is the length of a full-sized billiard table?
3 Which professional holds the record for the highest ever break – 4137?
4 Whom did Fred Davis beat to first win the World Professional title?
5 Who was the first known owner of a billiard table?
6 Did Joe Davis ever win the World Professional Billiards title?
7 Who was the Indian who regained his World Amateur Billiards title in 1981?
8 Who won the World Professional Billiards title in 1971, 1974 and 1976?
9 In which year did Fred Davis first win the World Professional Billiards Championship?
10 Which Briton was World Amateur Billiards Champion in 1971 and 1975?

BOB-SLEIGHING

1 Over how many runs are the aggregate times taken into account in a bobsleighing tournament?
2 Name the two Britons who won the gold medal in the two-man bob at the 1964 Olympics?
3 Which gold medallist from the summer Olympics of 1968 took part in the United States four-man bob team at the 1980 Lake Placid Games?
4 Is it the front axle or the rear axle that steers the bob?
5 What is the minimum number of banked turns there must be on a championship course?
6 In which countries can the following bob courses be found?
(a) Cortina d'Ampezzo (b) Garmisch Partenkirchen (c) Igls
7 Why does a driver always turn his head just before he comes into a bend?
8 The world's first bob run was built in 1902. Where?
9 Whose international career finished at the 1968 Olympics with two gold medals, after he had already won nine World titles?
10 What is the minimum distance for an international bob run?
11 How often are the World Championships held?
12 Which country has won most two-man bob World Championships?
13 Which country has won most four-man bob World Championships?
14 Which was the last country (before 1982) to complete the two-man and four-man bob 'double' at the World Championships?

BOWLS

1 Which Test cricketer was the first President of the English Bowling Association in 1903?

2 In a game of flat-green bowls, what is the minimum distance that the jack must travel from the mat?

3 The christian name of the winner of the 1980 Waterloo Tournament was the same as the surname of the man he beat in the final. What was it?

4 Who was the last man to win the Waterloo Cup twice?

5 Which Briton was the first winner, in 1966, of the World Bowls title?

6 In which town is the Waterloo Hotel – the home of the famous Waterloo Handicap – situated?

7 What term used to be used to describe a match involving eight players, now known as a fours?

8 How many woods does each man have in a game of singles in flat-green bowls?

9 Give either of the two other names by which the jack is known?

10 Who was the Welshman who won the World Bowls title in 1972?

11 What is the name of the trophy teams contest at the World Championships every four years?

12 In which city was the first World Men's Championships held in 1966?

13 Which country won all five titles at the 1976 World Bowls Championships?

14 Who has won the first three men's World Indoor Bowls Championships?

BOXING

IN WHAT YEAR?

Identify the correct years in which each of the following events took place?

1	Cassius Clay wins Olympic title	(a)	1976
2	WBC cruiserweight division first introduced	(b)	1964
3	Freddie Mills wins World Light Heavyweight title	(c)	1978
4	Alan Minter beat Kevin Finnegan to win Lonsdale Belt outright	(d)	1957
5	Cassius Clay first wins World Heavyweight title	(e)	1977
6	Henry Cooper has first British Heavyweight title fight	(f)	1960
7	Charlie Magri wins British title in his third professional fight	(g)	1979
8	Larry Holmes first wins WBC Heavyweight title	(h)	1948

NICKNAMES

1 Which former World Heavyweight Champion was nicknamed the 'Boston Strong Boy'?

2 . . . and which World Heavyweight Champion was known as the 'Cinderella Man'?

3 Two boxers with the name of Jack Dempsey have held World titles. One held the Heavyweight title, and one the Middleweight title – but by what nickname was the Middleweight Champion known?

4 Muhammad Ali was known as the 'Louisville Lip', but which British boxer was known as the 'Liverpool Lip'?

5 Which famous fighter was known as the 'Brockton Blockbuster'?

6 A three-times World Champion, he was nicknamed 'Homicide Hank'?

7 Who was Henry Cooper's long-standing manager, known as 'The Bishop'?

BOXING

THE NAME'S THE SAME

Identify the following boxers, all with the same names!

1 Two men with the same christian names and same surname, one won the World Middleweight title in 1894 and the other took the World Heavyweight title in 1919. Name them.
2 He was disqualified in a World Heavyweight title fight with Joe Louis in 1941, seven years after his brother had held the World title at the same weight. Give the surname.
3 Two unrelated postwar British Heavyweight Champions had the same surname. Name it.
4 They had the same surname, and in 1978 one was the WBC Light Heavyweight World Champion, and the other was British Middleweight Champion. Name them.
5 Same surname again – one was World Light Middleweight Champion in 1952 and the other was World Featherweight Champion in 1959. Name them.

WHICH COUNTRY?

The following World title fights were the first to be staged in one of 10 different countries. Name the countries concerned.

	Year	Fighters
1	1908	Tommy Burns v. Jem Roache
2	1962	Harold Johnson v. Gustav Scholtz
3	1971	Nino Benvenuti v. Tom Bethea
4	1964	Sugar Ramos v. Floyd Robertson
5	1963	Dick Tiger v. Gene Fullmer
6	1962	Eder Jofre v. Pierro Rollo
7	1962	Davey Moore v. Ollie Maeki
8	1947	Manuel Ortiz v. David Kui King
9	1937	Benny Lynch v. Peter Kane
10	1890	George Dixon v. Nunc Wallace

A MIXED BAG

1 Who was the last European to hold the World Heavyweight title?
2 If a boxer fails to make the weight at the weigh-in, how long is he allowed to make the weight?
3 Who was the last British boxer to win an Olympic title?
4 Who was the World Heavyweight Champion who won the 1952 Olympic Middleweight title at the age of 17?
5 Who was manager of former World Champion Maurice Hope?
6 Who was the first coloured boxer to win the World Heavyweight title?
7 How many World title fights did Muhammad Ali fight in under the name of Cassius Clay?
8 Which boxer once held World titles at three different weights all at the same time?
9 Only two boxers have won the Olympic Heavyweight title, and then gone on to win the Professional World Heavyweight title. Name them.
10 Who is the only man, other than Muhammad Ali, to lose and then regain the World Heavyweight title?

AT WHAT WEIGHT?

At what weight did each of the following men hold World titles in 1980? The weights and boxers are all mixed up – you have to identify which weight goes with which man.

1	Carlos de Leon	(a)	Featherweight
2	Marvin Hagler	(b)	Bantamweight
3	Sugar Ray Leonard	(c)	Light middleweight
4	Salvador Sanchez	(d)	Heavyweight
5	Matt Saeed Muhammed	(e)	Cruiserweight
6	Wilfredo Gomez	(f)	Light heavyweight
7	Lupe Pintor	(g)	Middleweight
8	Maurice Hope	(h)	Lightweight
9	Jim Watt	(i)	Super bantamweight
10	Mike Weaver	(j)	Welterweight

PICTURE QUIZ 1

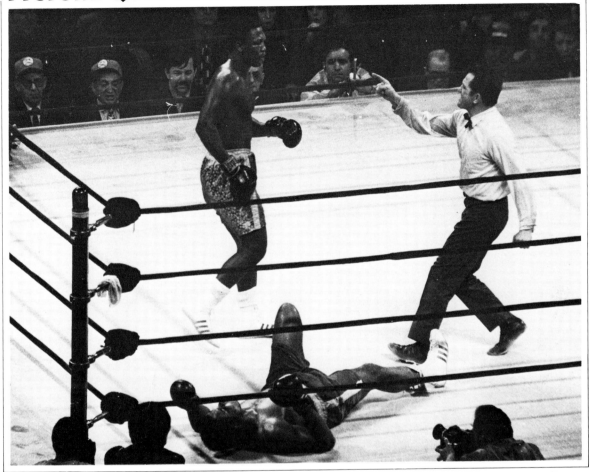

1 Who is the boxer on the floor against Joe Frazier?
2 Where did the fight take place?
3 In which year did the fight take place?

4 In which round was this photo taken?
5 Against which boxer did Frazier have his last successful World title defence?

IN WHICH ROUND?

In which round did the following World title fights finish?

1 The first Cassius Clay–Sonny Liston World Heavyweight title fight in 1964.
2 The John Conteh– Lenny Hutchins World Light Heavyweight title fight at Liverpool in 1977.

3 The Alan Minter fight against Vito Antuofermo when Minter took the World Middleweight title in 1980.
4 The Eckhard Dagge–Maurice Hope World Light Middleweight title fight in 1977.
5 Larry Holmes's World Heavyweight title fight in 1980 against Muhammad Ali – Ali's last crack at the World title.
6 The Jim Watt–Charlie Nash World Lightweight title fight in 1980.

BOXING

SO YOU THINK YOU KNOW MUHAMMAD ALI?

1 The last World Heavyweight title fight to be staged in England was between Ali, and which other man?

2 After he successfully defended his World title against Sonny Liston, who did Ali fight next?

3 Who was the first man to defeat him in a professional fight?

4 Where did Ali fight George Foreman for the World title in September 1974?

5 Who, in March 1973, had the audacity to break Ali's jaw?

6 Who, in March 1966, was the first man to take Ali 15 rounds?

7 Ali only fought one man both before and after winning the World title for the first time. Name his opponent.

8 Who was his last opponent before he had his World title taken away from him by the two major boxing authorities?

9 After changing his name from Cassius Clay, who was his first opponent?

10 At which venue did he fight Henry Cooper for the World title in 1966?

WHO WAS IT?

1 Against which boxer did Cassius Clay have his first fight outside the United States?

2 Who, in March 1977, became the first man to win the British Light Heavyweight title, after previously winning the Heavyweight title?

3 Who was the first coloured boxer to win a British title, when he beat Vince Hawkins for the Middleweight title in 1948?

4 Which boxer was killed in a plane crash in 1949 whilst on his way to a fight with Jake La Motta, four months after losing in a World Middleweight title fight to La Motta?

5 Who did John Conteh beat in 1974 to become the first Briton for over 25 years to hold the World Light Heavyweight title?

6 Who was the famous referee of the 1896 Tom Sharkey–Bob Fitzsimmons World Heavyweight title fight who had to pull a gun on Fitzsimmons to shut him up following his incessant protests to the referee?

7 Marvin Hagler, conqueror of Alan Minter in 1980, hails from the same town as which postwar World Heavyweight Champion?

8 He beat Max Schmelling to win the World Heavyweight title, and lost it to Primo Carnera. Name him.

9 Whom did John Conteh lose to over 15 rounds in his first attempt to regain the World Light Heavyweight title in June 1978?

10 Excluding Bob Fitzimmons, only two British boxers have gone the distance in World Heavyweight title fights. Name them.

VENUES

Name the venues of the following famous fights:

1 Jesse Willard *v.* Jack Johnson World Heavyweight title fight in 1915.

2 The 1976 World Light Heavyweight title fight between John Conteh and Alvarro Lopez.

3 In which city did Alan Minter beat Vito Antuofermo to win the World Middleweight title in 1980?

4 The 1978 Commonwealth Middleweight title fight between Ayub Kalule (Uganda) and Al Korovou (Australia and Fiji).

5 The 1965 World Heavyweight title fight that attracted the lowest ever crowd for a World Heavyweight title fight – between Sonny Liston and Muhammad Ali.

6 In which city did Terry Downes fail to win the World Light Heavyweight title in 1964?

7 John H. Stracey beat Jose Napoles to win the WBC Welterweight title in 1975 – in which city?

8 In which city did the 1976 World Heavyweight title fight between Muhammad Ali and Richard Dunn take place?

PICTURE QUIZ 2

1 Name the fighter from whom Maurice Hope won the World title?
2 To whom did Hope lose his World title?
3 Against whom did Hope have his first successful defence of his World title?
4 The photo shows Alan Minter in action as an amateur. Who foiled his attempt to win a 1972 Olympic gold medal?
5 Who is the boxer Minter is fighting in the photo?
6 What was the result?
7 Name the two former British Champions fought by Minter's opponent in 1981–2?
8 John Conteh on the way to the World title. Against whom?
9 Who was the holder of the other version of the title the night Conteh won the World title?
10 In four of Conteh's seven World title fights, the gong sounded for the 15th round. One was the night he won the title. Who were the other three opponents?

Maurice Hope

Alan Minter

John Conteh

PICTURE QUIZ 3

1 Who is the fighter?
2 Which film was based loosely on his life?
3 What was the result of his World title fight?

PICTURE QUIZ 4

1 Who is this former World Champion that Joe Bugner has floored?
2 Bugner fought Muhammad Ali twice – name the venues.
3 Who beat Bugner in two rounds in 1982?
4 Who took over as European Champion after Bugner's last reign?
5 Bugner fought Joe Frazier. What was the result and distance?

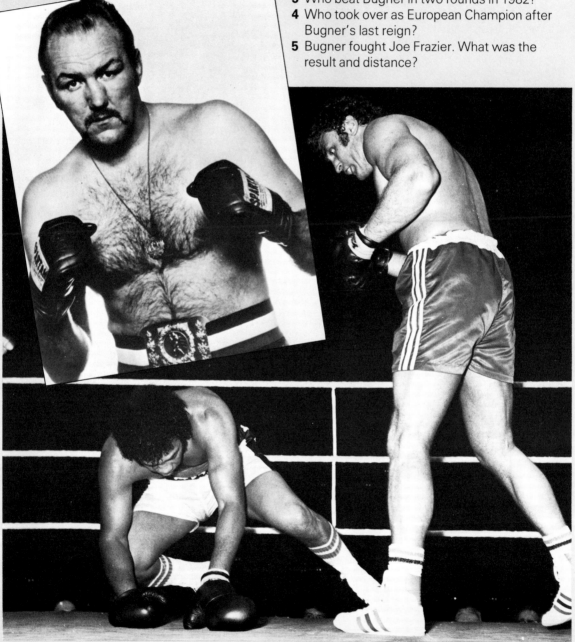

RULE BRITANNIA

All the following questions concern Britons who have been involved in World title fights:

1 Which Briton beat Salvatorre Burruni to win the World Flyweight title in 1966?

2 Who is the only British-born fighter to have won the World Heavyweight title?

3 Which Briton won the World Middleweight title in 1960?

4 Who lost his World title to Carlos Palomino in 1976?

5 Which Briton fought Sugar Ray Leonard for the World Welterweight title in 1980?

6 Whom did Maurice Hope outpoint to retain his title?

7 Who was the only British boxer to have fought Floyd Patterson for the World Heavyweight title?

8 Who was the first Briton after the last war to fight for the World Heavyweight title, when he fought Rocky Marciano?

BRITISH CHAMPIONS

Listed below is the beaten man in a British title fight, and the year concerned. You have to name the man who beat him to win a British title for the first time.

	Weight	Beaten man	Year
1	Light heavy	Eddie Avoth	1971
2	Welter	Wally Swift	1960
3	Heavy	Billy Aird	1978
4	Middle	Phil Edwards	1958
5	Light Middle	Bobby Arthur	1973
6	Heavy	Johnny Williams	1953
7	Light	Joe Lucy	1957
8	Heavy	Brian London	1959
9	Feather	Dave Needham	1979
10	Middle	Kevin Finnegan	1975

CANOEING & KAYAKING

1 The first ever canoe club, the Royal Canoe Club, was founded in 1866. In which country?

2 What are the main differences between canoeing and kayaking?

3 Who was the Swede who won six Olympic gold medals, spanning four games?

4 Name four of the five events that were contested in the 1980 Olympic canoeing competition.

5 What variation of a ball game, but played in canoes, held its first British championships at Crystal Palace in 1969?

6 Canoe races are divided into three categories. The slalom is one. Name either of the other two.

7 What is the distance of a Slalom course?

8 What is the maximum number of persons allowed in one canoe in international competitions?

9 Who was the Briton who became World Canoe Slalom Champion in 1977?

10 Where did the 1981 World Wild Water Championships take place?

11 Where were the 1982 World Championships held?

12 In which event was the British team disqualified for 'sinking' the Swedish and Yugoslav boats at the 1982 World Championships, losing the silver medal?

13 Who is the reigning World Men's Sprint Champion (K1)?

14 Who is the reigning Women's Sprint Champion (K1)?

15 True or false? All the 1980 Olympic canoeing champions were from Iron Curtain countries?

16 Gert Fredericksson won gold medals in four consecutive Olympics – which years?

CRICKET

PICTURE QUIZ 1

1 Name the bowler.
2 Name the gentleman relaxing with his daughter.
3 Name the batsman.

A MIXED BAG

1 Which county, other than Surrey, did Jim Laker play for?
2 Which bowler holds the record for taking the most number of wickets in a first-class career?
3 In which country are the Shell Cup and the Shell Trophy contested?
4 Which bowler was flown out as a replacement for the injured Bob Willis on the 1980–81 tour of the West Indies?
5 For which county did the legendary Wally Hammond play?
6 Who was the first cricketer to receive a benefit in excess of £100,000?
7 Who scored a century for Australia in the 1977 Centenary Test?
8 Which man holds the record for scoring the highest individual Test innings at four different Test centres?
9 Who were the very first winners of the John Player League?
10 Which man scored a century in the 1979 Prudential World Cup Final?

THE NAME'S THE SAME

Identify the surname of the following five sets of famous cricketers from the clues given:

1 A Middlesex batsman, and a former South African Test cricketer?
2 A postwar England captain, and a former Gloucestershire player who once took seven catches in an innings?
3 A Surrey and England player, and a Middlesex and England player. They were related, and both scored over 35,000 first-class runs?
4 A Surrey and England cricketer who played Test cricket at the age of 47, and an Essex and Glamorgan player who scored a 44-minute century against the Australians?
5 Essex and Derbyshire players who have each claimed over 1000 first-class victims?

CRICKET

INITIALS

Connect the initials of famous cricketers with the surnames:

1 D. C. S.		(a)	Cowdrey
2 W. G.		(b)	Close
3 D. G.		(c)	Compton
4 P. B. H.		(d)	Grace
5 M. C.		(e)	Lillee
6 D. B.		(f)	Harvey
7 F. S.		(g)	Bradman
8 R. N.		(h)	May
9 D. K.		(i)	Lock
10 G. A. R.		(j)	Trueman

DO YOU REMEMBER THE 1981 SEASON?

1 Who were the Minor Counties Champions?
2 Which man in 1981, became only the second man to have scored a century against all 17 first-class counties?
3 By how many points did Notts win the County Championship?
4 . . . and which county finished runners up to Notts in the Championship?
5 . . . and, talking of Notts, who captained them to that County Championship win?
6 Who was the only Australian to score two centuries in the England–Australia Test series?
7 Which Englishman reached the milestone of 30,000 first-class runs in 1981?
8 Who was the only bowler to take 100 wickets in 1981?
9 Who were the John Player League Champions?
10 Who was the first man to score 2000 runs during the season?
11 Who was the only man to score two Test double centuries in 1981?
12 Which man scored a century on his Test debut in 1981?

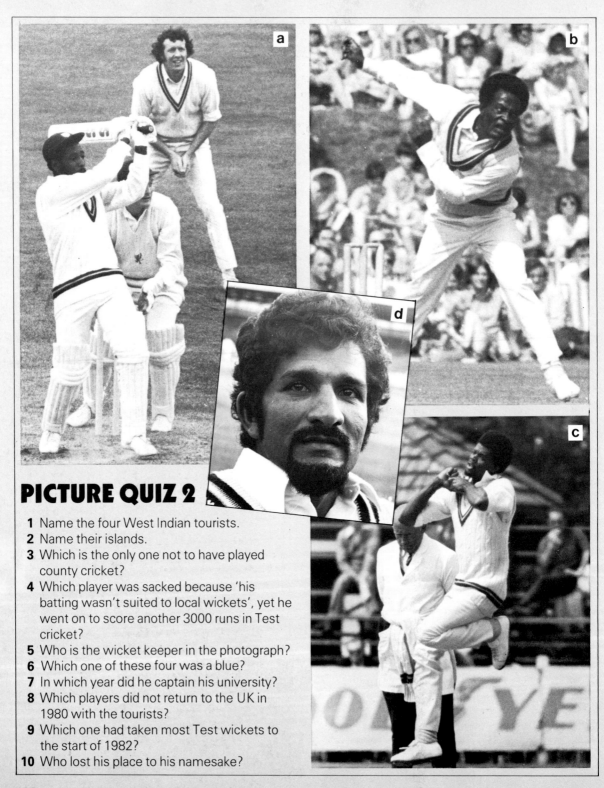

PICTURE QUIZ 2

1. Name the four West Indian tourists.
2. Name their islands.
3. Which is the only one not to have played county cricket?
4. Which player was sacked because 'his batting wasn't suited to local wickets', yet he went on to score another 3000 runs in Test cricket?
5. Who is the wicket keeper in the photograph?
6. Which one of these four was a blue?
7. In which year did he captain his university?
8. Which players did not return to the UK in 1980 with the tourists?
9. Which one had taken most Test wickets to the start of 1982?
10. Who lost his place to his namesake?

PLAYERS AND COUNTRIES

Which player in each group did not play for the country shown?

1 *England*
  (a) K. S. Duleepsinhji
  (b) C. Hill
  (c) P. F. Warner
2 *Australia*
  (a) D. Wellham
  (b) D. W. Hookes
  (c) S. F. Barnes
3 *India*
  (a) P. Roy
  (b) A. V. Mankad
  (c) R. Abel
4 *Pakistan*
  (a) D. Sharpe
  (b) A. D. Gaekwad
  (c) Nasim Ul Ghani
5 *New Zealand*
  (a) W. M. Darling
  (b) J. R. Reid
  (c) V. Pollard
6 *West Indies*
  (a) S. Ramadhin
  (b) J. M. Parker
  (c) J. S. Solomon
7 *South Africa*
  (a) A. D. Nourse
  (b) H. J. Tayfield
  (c) S. M. Nurse

HOW MANY?

1 How many Test centuries did W. G. Grace score in his career: 2; 18; 65?
2 How many runs did Gary Sobers score when he established the record for the highest individual Test innings: 364; 365; 499?
3 How many runs did Australia beat England by in the very first Test match in 1877, and also by the same margin in the centenary Test: 12; 29; 45?

CRICKET

4 How many times did Lancashire win the Gillette Cup: 4; 5; 6?
5 How many times did Colin Cowdrey play for England: 101; 114; 137?
6 How many hundreds did Denis Compton score in 1947, when he established a new record for the most centuries in one season: 15; 18; 21?
7 How many teams play in the Minor Counties Championship: 15; 18; 21?
8 How many points are awarded for a win in the County Championship: 10; 15; 16?

WHICH GROUND?

1 On which ground did Peter Loader, in 1957, become the last man to perform the hat trick for England?
2 On which ground did England play the West Indies for the first time in 1980–81?
3 Two non-Test grounds have staged Prudential One-Day Test matches in this country. Name them.
4 Lancashire play their County Championship matches at four grounds. Manchester, Blackpool, and Liverpool are three. Name the fourth.
5 Which centre became the 50th Test centre in 1979?
6 On which ground did Don Bradman score two Test triple centuries?
7 At which Test ground would you find the Radcliffe Road End?
8 Which ground has staged just one Test Match in England?
9 Which is the most northerly ground in England upon which County Championship cricket is played?
10 Which Test ground is owned by H R H Prince Charles?

PICTURE QUIZ 3

1 Name the players.
2 Name their states.
3 Which player took 6–14 in a World Cup game?
4 Which player made four tours to England?
5 What did one of these players remarkably achieve at Lords in 1972?
6 Who was bowled by the only ball he faced in the 15-match tour to England in 1975?
7 Which player was turned down by Northants?
8 Of the four, who played in the least number of Tests?
9 Which of the four played first-class Australian-rules football?
10 All four bowled in Test cricket. Who has taken most wickets to the start of 1982?
11 . . . and the least?

A MIXED BAG FOR THE EXPERT

1 Which player once scored 1000 runs and took 200 wickets in a season for three consecutive years?
2 Which was the first county, in 1973, to lose to a university side in the Benson and Hedges Cup?
3 Who is the youngest player to have scored a Test double century?
4 Which England bowler had figures of 11 for 145 on his Test debut against India in 1946?
5 Who was the New Zealand bowler who dismissed Geoff Boycott for two ducks in 1969?
6 Greg Chappell, with 631, scored the most runs in aggregate in the Kerry Packer Supertests – but who, with 363, was second to him?
7 Who scored a century in the only Test Match to be played at Bramall Lane, Sheffield?
8 Which umpire has stood in the most number of Test Matches?
9 Who was the South African wicketkeeper involved in the Len Hutton 'obstructing the field' incident in 1951?
10 Who was the first man to score a century in the John Player League?
11 Who gained selection to the Australian squad to tour England in 1961 despite the fact that he had only played 11 first-class matches at the time?
12 Which was the last county before Lancashire to appear in three successive Gillette Cup Finals?
13 Which man has reached the milestone of 100 Test wickets in the least number of matches – 16?
14 Which bowler took 7 for 15 for Yorkshire in a John Player League game against Worcestershire in 1969?
15 Which batsman holds the record for reaching 30,000 first-class runs in the least number of matches – 373?

SO YOU THINK YOU KNOW THE GILLETTE CUP?

1 Who beat Derbyshire in their last appearance in 1969?
2 Which man has scored the highest individual innings in the final of the competition?
3 Which was the first county to appear in three finals?
4 Who holds the record for scoring the fastest century in the competition?
5 Only two men won the Man of the Match award in the final after finishing on the losing side. Name them.
6 Which is the only county to have made a total in excess of 300 in the final of the competition?
7 Who is the only man to take 40 wickets and score over 1000 runs in the Gillette Cup?
8 Who is the only man to have scored four centuries in the competition?
9 Which was the first Minor County to reach the third round of the Cup?
10 Who is the only man to have taken six wickets in a final?
11 . . . and who was the last man to score a century in a final?
12 Who captained Worcestershire to defeat in the very first final in 1963?
13 Who is the only man to have won two Man of the Match awards in the final?
14 Which wicketkeeper has claimed the most victims in the competition?
15 . . . and which bowler has taken the most wickets in the competition?
16 Which was the last team to complete the winning of the County Championship and Gillette Cup in the same year?
17 Which was the second county to win the Gillette Cup?
18 Who won the Gillette Cup in 1976?
19 . . . and who was Man of the Match in the 1979 final?
20 How many times have Lancashire won the cup?

CURLING

1 Which country has won the World Championships on the greatest number of occasions?
2 The country of origin of curling is not exactly known, but two countries lay claim to being its birthplace. Name either.
3 Curling is the ice-playing equivalent of what sport?
4 What is the name of the trophy awarded to the winners of the World Championships?
5 What name is given to a curling match played by a large gathering?
6 What name is given to the playing surface in a game of curling?
7 Over what distance does a curler throw the stone?
8 Which famous ice rink housed the first curling centre in England?
9 Who were the first winners of the Women's World Championships in 1980?
10 Which was the last European country to win the Men's World Championships?

PICTURE QUIZ

Who are the reigning World Women's Team Champions?

DARTS

1 What is the height from the floor to the centre of the bull?
2 Who was the unseeded Irishman who sprang a surprise by eliminating defending champion Eric Bristow in the first round of the 1982 World Championship?
3 Who was the first World Masters Champion in 1974?
4 Who was the 1981 *News of the World* Champion?
5 170 is the highest three-dart finish. Assuming a double to finish, what is the next highest?
6 Who is known as the 'Man in Black'?
7 Name the first winner of the *News of the World* darts title?
8 . . . and from which northern town did he hail?
9 Who captained the first ever women's England international team in 1977?
10 Who is the only man to have won the professional World title when *not* seeded Number One?
11 Who, in 1975, was the first winner of the British Open Championship?
12 What is the name of the club that houses the Embassy World Professional Championships each year?
13 Who is the only overseas player to have won the *News of the World* title?
14 Who is the only man to have won the professional World title twice?
15 Who was the overseas player who won the 1979 World Cup?
16 Who is the only Welshman before 1981 to have won the World Masters title?
17 Who is the British woman player who has twice won the North American Open?
18 Who is the only Englishman other than Eric Bristow to win the World Individual Championship?

FENCING

1 What are the three types of sword used in international fencing?
2 Who, at the 1956 Olympics, won Britain's first ever fencing gold medal?
3 Who was the Russian fencer disqualified for cheating during the modern pentathlon at the 1976 Montreal Olympics?
4 What are the forte and the foible on a sword?
5 What is the name given to a contest between two fencers?
6 What in fencing is the piste?
7 How many successful hits decides a winner in men's competitions?
8 Who was the Essex cricketer who represented Great Britain in the fencing competition at the Mexico and Munich Olympics?
9 In the épée event, what is the target area?
10 Was fencing included in the inaugural Olympic Games in 1896?
11 Who was the first Briton to win a World fencing title, in 1959 in the foil?
12 What is the name of the principal fencing centre in London?
13 Which country has won more fencing medals at the Olympics than any other?

PICTURE QUIZ

Which discipline is this?

GOLF

THE BRITISH OPEN

1 Who was the Briton who finished runner-up to Arnold Palmer in the 1961 Open at Birkdale?
2 Who played a memorable shot out of a broken bottle at the 1949 Open at Sandwich?
3 Henry Cotton won the British Open three times, and on each occasion he represented a different club: Ashridge, and Royal Mid-Surrey were two. Name the third.
4 There were three holes in one during the 1981 Open, and all three were at the same hole. Which?
5 Who, in 1907, was the first overseas player to win the Open?
6 Who finished runner-up to Tony Jacklin the year he won the Open?
7 Which was the last course to stage two successive British Opens?
8 Who was the last Irishman to win the Open?
9 The Morris family have eight British Open wins between them. Which other family can claim seven wins between them?
10 Peter Thompson won the Open in 1954, 1955, 1956 and 1958; he was runner-up in 1957. To whom?
11 The initial British Open was played over just three rounds – but how many holes were played in each round?
12 Who was the leading Briton in the 1981 British Open?
13 When Bob Charles won the 1963 British Open, whom did he beat in a play-off?
14 Only two Britons have won the silver medal for being the leading amateur in the Open since the last war. Peter McEvoy is one. Name the other.
15 Who was the Royal Liverpool golfer who was the first amateur to win the Open?

PICTURE QUIZ 1

1 Name the four major courses here.
2 Who holds the course record for 18 holes on the old course?
3 Which hole is referred to as the 'road hole'?
4 In which county is St Andrews?
5 Why is Mr L. Auchterlonie well known?

A MIXED BAG

1 Who is the only left-handed golfer to have won the British Open?
2 Who is the youngest person to have represented Great Britain in the Ryder Cup?
3 How often do the women golfers of the United States and Great Britain contest the Curtis Cup?
4 On which course did Tony Jacklin have his British Open success in 1969?
5 Who is the only Briton to have won the individual title in the World Cup?
6 Which man has captained the British Ryder Cup team on a record five occasions?
7 In golfing terms, what is an albatross?
8 Which club was Tony Jacklin representing at the time of his British Open success?
9 Who won himself a flat and furnishings, valued at £55,000, for holing in one during the 1979 World Match Play Championships?
10 Which course stages the World Match Play Championships every year?
11 Which Briton finished second to Gary Player in the 1974 British Open at Lytham?
12 Who was the last man to win the British Open three years in succession?
13 On which British Open course can the famous 'postage stamp' hole be found?
14 What nationality was former British Open winner Bobby Locke?
15 Which golfer has won the British Open on a record six occasions?

ON COURSE

1 Which course stages the US Masters annually?
2 Which course staged the British Open for the first time in 1977?
3 At which course did Tony Jacklin win the US Open?
4 Crans sur Sierre is the home of which European Open?
5 Which course staged the inaugural European Open in 1978?

GOLF

6 The only time the Ryder Cup was tied was in 1969 – on which British course?
7 Which course staged the very first British Open in 1860?
8 The Royal Liverpool golf course is *not* actually stituated in Liverpool. Where is it?

PICTURE QUIZ 2

1 In which year did Lee Trevino retain the British Open title?
2 In which year was he runner up in the British Open?

3 He won three major Opens in four weeks – the British Open, and the US Open. Which was the third?
4 What was the name of Edward Heath's famous yacht?
5 Which yachting classic has he won?

GOLF

IN WHAT YEAR?

Match up the correct years with the following golfing events:

1 First World Cup competition
   (formerly the Canada Cup)   (a) 1970
2 Tony Jacklin wins US Open   (b) 1957
3 First World Match Play Champ-
   ionships won by Arnold Palmer   (c) 1967
4 Jack Nicklaus wins
   his first British Open   (d) 1956
5 British Open played
   at Hoylake for the last time   (e) 1953
6 Maurice Bembridge records
   a round of 64 in the US Open   (f) 1964
7 Peter Thomson wins British
   Open for third successive year   (g) 1974
8 Great Britain
   last won the Ryder Cup outright   (h) 1966

A MIXED BAG FOR THE EXPERT

1 Who was the last man to win the British and United States Opens in the same season?
2 Which is the oldest championship in Britain, open to professional players *only*?
3 Who, in 1974, was the last Englishman to be leading money winner in Europe?
4 Who are the only father and son to have represented Britain in the Ryder Cup?
5 What is the name of the trophy awarded to the PGA member resident in the United Kingdom who returns the lowest round in the British Open?
6 Who is the only golfer in the 42-year history of the US Masters to have won the title in successive years?
7 Which is the longest course, at 7066 yards, on the British Open rota?

8 In which country was Peter Alliss born?
9 Sally Barber, British Curtis Cup player, is the sister of which well-known golfer?
10 Who was the Irishman who won his first international tournament in 1977, when he won the Kenyan Open?
11 Henry Longhurst was a scratch golfer, and indeed he won the Amateur Championship of which country in 1936?
12 Who captained the United States in each of the first six Ryder Cup matches?

PICTURE QUIZ 3

1 In how many Ryder Cups has Christy O'Connor played?
2 In which year was he second in the British Open?
3 And in which year was he third?
4 In which years was he World Seniors' Champion?
5 What major event did he win in 1958?

GREYHOUND RACING

1 What is the longest distance in yards over which races are run in Great Britain?
2 What is the maximum number of greyhounds that may run in one race?
3 What colours does the dog in trap 6 always wear?
4 Which track stages the Greyhound Derby each year?
5 . . . and over what distance (in metres) is the Greyhound Derby run?
6 Which was the last dog to win the Greyhound Derby two years in succession?
7 The Laurels, one of greyhound racing's classics, was first run in 1930. At which track is it run?
8 In which English city is the Perry Barr greyhound stadium?
9 Which dog is regarded as the greatest greyhound of all time, winning the Derby two years in succession in 1929 and 1930?
10 Where was the first greyhound track in Britain? It opened in 1926.

PICTURE QUIZ

Test your memory of some of the better known facts . . .
1 The 1982 Greyhound Derby winner?
2 Who owned Camira Flash, the 1968 winner?
3 In what year was the first Derby?
4 The first dog to retain the Derby?
5 In which year did India Joe win the Derby?

GYMNASTICS

1 Who was the Russian girl who finished second to Nadia Comaneci in the overall competition in the 1976 Olympics?
2 Who was the Russian man who won four individual gold medals at the 1960 Rome Olympics?

3 Which girl won three gold medals at the 1964 Olympics, and a further four in 1968?
4 Who was the Women's Overall Champion in 1978?
5 He was the overall winner in the men's events at the Montreal Olympics, and also won four individual gold medals. Name him.
6 How many individual gold medals did Olga Korbut win at the 1972 Games?
7 In which exercise did Nadia Comaneci and Nellie Kim share the gold medal at the 1980 Moscow Olympics?

PICTURE QUIZ

Olga Korbut ▲ and Ludmila Tourischeva ▶

1 To whom is Ludmila Tourischeva married?
2 What occupation has Olga Korbut's husband?
3 How many Olympic golds did Ludmila win?
4 . . . and how many Olympic golds did Olga win?
5 Who is the reigning Women's Olympic overall champion?

HOCKEY

1 How many players make up a hockey team?
2 What is the width of the goal in a hockey match?
3 Which country has won the Olympic hockey title on the greatest number of occasions?
4 Which country won the first ever Women's Olympic gold medal?
5 Which British side won the Men's European Championship in 1980?
6 What is the length of a hockey pitch?
7 In men's hockey they are called inside right and inside left. What are they called in women's hockey?
8 The first hockey club founded in England was in 1861. Where?
9 Which country won its first ever gold medal, at the 1980 Olympics, in the hockey tournament?
10 Who was the women's international who gained her 100th cap for England in the late 1970s?
11 How long is each half in a hockey match?
12 Which country won the 1976 men's Olympic hockey title?
13 The first-ever County Championship was instituted in 1957. Which county won that title?

PICTURE QUIZ

1 This is the 1973 World Cup final between Holland and India. Where was it staged?
2 In which year was the first World Cup staged?
3 And who won that first World Cup?
4 Which Dutchman won European Superstars in 1977 and 1978?
5 Who are the reigning Olympic champions?

HORSE RACING

THANKS FOR THE RIDE

The following horses provided the jockeys listed below them with their first ever English Classic win. You have to put the right jockey with the right Classic winner.

1 Polygamy (1974 Oaks)
2 Caergwrle (1968 1000 Guineas)
3 Glad Rags (1966 1000 Guineas)
4 Homeward Bound (1964 Oaks)
5 High Top (1972 2000 Guineas)
6 Right Tack (1969 2000 Guineas)
7 Cantelo (1959 St Leger)
8 Blakeney (1969 Derby)

  (a) Sandy Barclay
  (b) Willie Carson
  (c) Eddie Hide
  (d) Pat Eddery
  (e) Paul Cook
  (f) Ernie Johnson
  (g) Geoff Lewis
  (h) Greville Starkey

A MIXED BAG

1 Who was the last man before Willie Carson to ride three English Classic winners in one season?
2 What relation, if any, are Peter and Fulke Walwyn to each other?
3 The American Triple Crown consists of the Kentucky Derby, the Belmont Stakes, and which other race?
4 Which jockey, who had 2748 winners out of 8084 mounts, committed suicide at the age of 29?

5 Michael 'Mouse' Morris, the former Irish jockey, has a father famous in sporting circles the world over. Who is he?
6 Which trainer, in 1979, became the first to win over £1,000,000 in prize money under National Hunt rules?
7 What is the French Derby called?
8 Four champion jockeys have ridden Red Rum in public. Ron Barry, Tommy Stack and Josh Gifford are three. Name the fourth.
9 Which jockey in 1981 became the first to ride three different winners at three different meetings in the same day?
10 Who used to train the legendary Arkle?
11 In the King George VI and Queen Elizabeth Diamond Stakes what is the ratio of winners of three-year-old horses to four-year-old and above?

THE GRAND NATIONAL

1 Name the Aintree Grand National winner that was trained by Lester Piggott's father?
2 Who was the 17-year-old jockey who rode Battleship to victory in the 1938 Grand National?
3 A runner in the 1981 Grand National had the same name as the winner of the 1937 race. Name him.
4 He rode Royal Danieli into second place in the 1938 National, and trained L'Escargot to victory in the 1975 race. Name him.
5 Which horse, in 1965 and 1966, was the last horse before Red Rum to finish as runner up in the National two years in succession?
6 Who rode Reynoldstown to his second Grand National victory?
7 Which is the only horse to have won the Grand National at both Gatwick and Aintree?
8 The father of which champion flat race jockey rode the 1858 winner, Little Charlie?
9 Which horse finished fourth in the 1977 Grand National, fifth in 1978, and fourth again in 1979?
10 Who rode Ego into second place in the 1936 National, behind the winner, Reynoldstown?

PLAY YOUR MATE – FAMOUS RACES

A chance to pit your wits against a friend. Listed below are three postwar winners of famous races. Your three are on the left, your mate's are on the right. See how you do compared to him.

1 (a)
Wollow
High Top
Roland Gardens

(b)
Blustery
Kings Ride
Foggy Bell

2 (a)
Hula Dancer
Cairn Rouge
Flying Water

(b)
Son Of Love
Athens Wood
Light Cavalry

3 (a)
Larkspur
Relko
Nijinsky

(b)
L'Escargot
Kilmore
Specify

4 (a)
Hawaiian Sound
Beldale Flutter
Master Willie

(b)
Attivo
Sea Pigeon
John Cherry

5 (a)
Mrs McArdy
Highclere
Enstone Spark

(b)
Dahlia
Meadow Court
Grundy

6 (a)
Prince de Galles
Baronet
Intermission

(b)
Sea Pigeon
Protection Racket
Dakota

7 (a)
Captain Christy
Silver Buck
Bachelors Hall

(b)
Little Owl
Alverton
Midnight Court

8 (a)
Sassafrass
Star Appeal
Three Troixas

(b)
Youth
Nobiliary
Johnny D

HORSE RACING

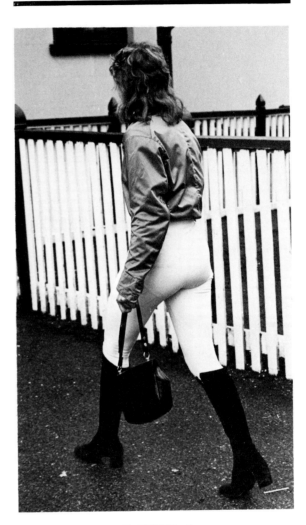

PICTURE QUIZ 1

1 What was the occasion?
2 On what course?
3 Who was the winning jockey?
4 On what horse?
5 At what price?
6 In which year?

A famous lady on a famous occasion. Name the occasion and the horse.

A MIXED BAG FOR THE EXPERT

1 On which track is the Preakness Stakes, the second leg of the American Triple Crown, run?

2 Which horse, in winning the 1950 Oaks, was the last maiden to win an English Classic?

3 Name either of the two horses to have won *four* English Classics.

4 Who was the first National Hunt trainer to win in excess of £50,000 in one season?

5 Who was the only jockey, other than Gordon Richards, to have been placed in an English Classic every year from 1945 to 1951 inclusive?

6 What did Vice-Admiral the Honourable Henry Rous give to racing?

7 Which was the first English Classic winner sired by Brigadier Gerard?

8 What is the French Oaks known as?

9 Who was the Australian rider who won an Olympic equestrian gold medal at the 1960 Rome Olympics, and five years later, on his own horse Stoney Crossing, he finished third in the Cheltenham Gold Cup behind Arkle and Mill House?

10 What was significant about Pat's victory in the South Coast Stakes at Brighton on 3 August 1966?

11 Which was the last horse Lester Piggott rode in public for Noel Murless?

12 Apart from Fred Archer and Gordon Richards, who is the only other man to have ridden over 200 winners on the flat in an English season?

13 Which man has been the sole owner of five Epsom Derby winners?

14 Only four horses ever beat Arkle in a steeplechase. Dormant, Stalbridge Colonist and Mill House were three. Name the fourth.

15 Which woman, in 1978, became the first female *professional* jockey to ride a winner in this country?

WHO AM I?

Identify the following two horse-racing personalities from the three clues given in each case:

1 *Clue 1*: Born 1926, my career as a jockey spanned 25 years from 1939 to 1964. I won the Grand National twice, and the Cheltenham Gold Cup twice.

Clue 2: I obtained my trainer's licence in 1964 and have since trained two Grand National winners, and a Cheltenham Gold Cup winner, the late Lanzarrotte being one of the best horses I have ever trained.

Clue 3: My first jockey at present is the successful Johnny Francome – and together we won the 1978 Cheltenham Gold Cup with Midnight Court.

2 *Clue 1*: Born in 1934, one of a pair of racing brothers. My brother sadly lost his life on the race track.

Clue 2: I had my first English Classic win in the 1953 Oaks on Ambiguity.

Clue 3: 1979 was my best ever year: I rode One in a Million to victory in the 1000 Guineas.

HORSES FOR COURSES

Questions concerning racecourses.

1 On which course did the Scottish National used to be run before moving to its present home at Ayr in 1966?
2 The 1940 St Leger was not run at Doncaster. Where was it staged?
3 On which course is the Durham National run?
4 On which course is the Prix de l'Arc de Triomphe run?
5 Lord Hesketh, of motor-racing fame, is the owner of which racecourse?

HORSE RACING

6 On which course is the Fighting Fifth Hurdle normally run?
7 In which park are the Longchamps and Auteil courses?
8 What jumping course stages racing on the first and last days of every National Hunt season?
9 Name the only racecourse in Yorkshire that does not stage flat racing?
10 On which course is the 'Midlands' Grand National run?

RACING CERTAINTIES

1 The Autumn Double consists of the Cesarewitch and which other race?
2 How many fences are jumped twice on the Aintree Grand National course?
3 A champion jockey on the flat in recent years, he was champion apprentice as recently as 1971. Name him.
4 Which was the last 100 to 1 winner of the Aintree Grand National?
5 The first race meeting in this country was held in 1511. At which course?
6 Who, in 1952, was the last jockey to ride over 200 winners in a flat racing season in this country?
7 Which English racecourse is often referred to as the Knavesmire?
8 Which man rode Red Rum to two Grand National victories?
9 What relation is trainer Robert Armstrong to Lester Piggott?
10 Who was the first jockey ever to win over $5 million in prize money in one season?

PICTURE QUIZ 3

Who are the jockeys and in which years were they
last champion jockey before 1982?

SO YOU THINK YOU KNOW THE DERBY?

1 Who is the youngest person this century to have ridden an Epsom Derby winner?
2 Which man trained the 1982 Epsom Derby winner?
3 Which horse started as favourite for the 1977 Derby having never lost a race, yet only finished third?
4 Since the war, only two jockeys have ridden three Derby winners. One is Lester Piggott, of course. Name the other.
5 Which horse won the 1913 Derby, but was subsequently disqualified?
6 Who was the last trainer to saddle two successive Derby winners?
7 Lester Piggott and who else rode two Derby winners in the 1960s?
8 Who was the first man after the last war to ride two successive Derby winners?
9 Which jockey had his first ever ride in the Epsom Derby in 1978 at the tender age of 46?
10 Since the war which trainer has had the misfortune of losing the Epsom Derby twice on a photo finish?

CLOSED COURSES

Questions concerning now-defunct British courses:

1 Currently the site of a British Airport, it has staged the Grand National. Name it.
2 Which was the last racecourse in Britain to close down before Stockton in 1981?
3 Which famous course closed down following its very last meeting on 8 September 1970?
4 Which now-defunct racecourse staged the last Welsh Grand National before the last war?
5 . . . and which other now-defunct course staged the Welsh National immediately prior to its moving to its present home at Chepstow in 1949?

HORSE RACING

IDENTIFY THE FOLLOWING COURSES

PICTURE QUIZ 4

1 Which Classic course is this?
2 What is the length of the Classic course?
3 Who was the last Frenchman before 1982 to ride the winner of the Classic?
4 Which was the Queen's last Classic winner here?
5 . . . and Edward Hide's last Classic winner here?

WHO PARTNERED THEM?

Which one of the three jockeys rode each of the following horses to famous victories?

1 Tap on Wood, 1979 2000 Guineas: Steve Cauthen; Willie Shoemaker; Walter Swinburn
2 Nijinsky, 1970 Derby: Scobie Breasley; Ron Hutchinson; Lester Piggott
3 Grundy, 1975 Derby: Pat Eddery; Willie Carson; Frankie Durr
4 Red Rum, 1977 Grand National: Jonjo O'Neill; Tommy Stack; Brian Fletcher
5 Brigadier Gerard, 1972 King George VI and Queen Elizabeth II Diamond Stakes: Sandy Barclay; Paul Cook; Joe Mercer
6 Dunfermline, 1977 Oaks: Tony Murray; Willie Carson; Greville Starkey
7 Mill Reef, 1971 Prix de L'Arc de Triomphe: Geoff Lewis; Bruce Raymond; Paul Cook
8 Arkle – 1964, 1965 and 1966 Cheltenham Gold Cup: Paddy Broderick; Terry Biddlecombe; Pat Taafe

ICE HOCKEY

A MIXED BAG

1 How many players are in an ice hockey team?
2 The start of a field hockey game is called a bully off, but what is it called in a game of ice hockey?
3 How many referees are there in international ice hockey matches?
4 A game is split into three periods – each lasting how long?
5 What is the minimum period for which a player can be sent to the sin bin?
6 In which country did ice hockey originate?
7 What is North America's premier ice hockey trophy called?
8 Roy Halpin scored 14 goals in his side's 24–1 win in a British League match against Durham Wasps in 1982. What team was he playing for at the time?
9 Ice hockey was first introduced into the Olympic programme in 1920, and Canada were the first four winners of the title. Which country ended their domination?
10 Which team won the British Ice Hockey League in 1981–82?

MIX AND MATCH

The Stanley Cup has been competed for since 1893, and is the premier professional hockey tournament. Since 1965 there have been just five winners. On the left is the city and on the right the name of the club. Test your knowledge.

1	Montreal	(a)	Flyers
2	Toronto	(b)	Islanders
3	Boston	(c)	Canadians
4	New York	(d)	Maple Leafs
5	Philadelphia	(e)	Bruins

ICE SKATING

TAKE YOUR PARTNERS

Marry up the following with their correct partners:

1	Christopher Dean	(a)	Tai Babalonia
2	Randy Gardner	(b)	Doreen Denny
3	Warren Maxwell	(c)	Hilary Green
4	Courtney Jones	(d)	Diane Towler
5	Glynn Watts	(e)	Janet Thompson
6	Bernard Ford	(f)	Jayne Torvill

FOR THE EXPERT: WORLD AND OLYMPIC CHAMPIONS

1 Who was the last man to win the Olympic title but not that year's World title?
2 What nationality was former World Champion Ondrej Nepela?
3 Irina Rodnina has won the Olympic pairs title with two men – Alex Zaitsev, and who else?
4 He first won the men's World title in 1974, and for the second time in 1980. Name him.
5 Which man holds the record for the most World title wins, and also has a 'movement' named after him?
6 Who was the Russian who was second to John Curry in the 1976 World Championship, and won the event in 1977?
7 When John Curry won the 1976 Olympic men's title, who won the ladies' title?
8 Who was the last male skater to win the World Championship three years in a row?
9 And who was the last woman to win the World Championship on three consecutive occasions.?

PICTURE QUIZ

1 Four famous photos of people in the ice skating world. Who are they?
2 How many times were the ice dance pair above World Champions . . . ?
3 . . . and who was the girl's other partner with whom she won World titles?
4 Whom did Robin Cousins succeed as Olympic Champion?
5 Whom did the coach train to be World Champion in 1979?
6 Which is Robin Cousins's home town?

c

ICE SKATING

GREAT BRITONS

Questions concerning British skaters.

1 Who was the leading British male skater in the 1981 European Championships at Innsbruck?
2 Prior to John Curry, the last person to win an ice-skating gold medal for Britain at the Olympics was in the ladies' figure skating at the 1952 Games. Name the woman who won the medal for us.
3 In what year did John Curry have his triple crown success?
4 In which city did Robin Cousins train?
5 Who was the British girl who led the 1981 European Championships going into the final round, but then suffered a series of disasters, to end up in sixth place?

d

JUDO

1 There are two grades in judo – the Dan, and which other?
2 Name the two Britons who won medals at the 1976 Montreal Olympics?
3 Who was the British girl who won the World title in 1980?
4 . . . and, who in 1981, was the first British male to win the World title?
5 What was the nationality of Anton Geesink, winner of the 1964 Olympic open class gold medal?
6 The minimum weight for an Olympic heavyweight boxer is 81 kilogrammes (12 stone 10 pounds). Is the minimum weight for a judo heavyweight heavier or lighter?
7 What name is given to a judo contest?
8 The mat in a judo contest is always square. What size is it?
9 The top grade in Judo is the 12th Dan. What colour belt does he wear?
10 In what year was judo first included in the Olympic programme?

PICTURE QUIZ 1

1 Name the two judo players.
2 Which Olympic medals did they win?
3 How many weight categories were contested at the 1980 Olympics?

PICTURE QUIZ 2

A photograph of Japan's most famous current exponent of Judo. He's the World Heavyweight Champion. Who is he?

KARATE

1 In a karate contest, there is one referee, and how many judges?
2 Which country, in the 1972 World Championships, became the first to beat Japan in an international?
3 What is the name given to the 'wood beating' aspect of karate?
4 Which country won the World team title in 1975?
5 What colour belt do novices wear?
6 The area upon which a karate contest is held is always square, but is variable in size. The minimum size is 26 × 26 feet. What is the maximum?
7 Each judge has three important pieces of equipment on him. Name them.
8 In an international competition, if a dispute arises, who is the only person allowed to query a referee's decision?
9 Despite the sport's ancient origins, the first organized World Championships were held in postwar years. Were they staged in 1949, 1960, 1970 or 1975?
10 What would a karate expert do with a makiwara?

LAWN TENNIS

A MIXED BAG

1 Who was the 1982 Wimbledon referee?
2 Manuel Orantes won the 1975 United States Open. Who was his fellow countryman who won the French Open title three years earlier?
3 What was the maiden name of Mrs Cawley who won the Wimbledon ladies' doubles title in 1977?
4 Who had his one and only major men's singles victory in 1966 when he won the French Open?
5 Who was the last amateur to reach the men's singles semifinals at Wimbledon?
6 Who, in 1965, were the first brother and sister to be ranked in the top ten in the United States in the same year?
7 Who was the last man, before John McEnroe in 1981, to defeat Bjorn Born in the men's singles at Wimbledon?
8 Who was the last man before John McEnroe to win three successive United States titles?
9 Which stadium houses the French championships each year?
10 Who was the last woman to beat Christine Truman in the ladies' singles at Wimbledon?
11 Who was the unseeded player beaten in the semifinal of the men's singles by John McEnroe in 1981 at Wimbledon?
12 Who was the very first men's singles champion at Wimbledon in 1877?
13 Jimmy Connors, in winning the WCT final in 1980, became only the second man to win the final on two occasions. Name the other.
14 Who, in 1979, became the first pair of brothers to win the men's doubles at one of the world's major tournaments, since the 1920s?
15 Which man holds the record (60) for winning the most singles matches at Wimbledon?

55

PICTURE QUIZ 1

1 Mark Edmondson in the crowd. In which year did he win his only grand slam event, the Australian Open?
2 Who is this chewing the ball?

WIMBLEDON WINNERS

1 Who were the last pair to win the men's doubles at Wimbledon three years in succession?
2 Who did Virginia Wade beat in the ladies' singles final in 1977?
3 Who won the first singles final to be decided on a tie breaker?
4 Who is the only man to have won the junior Wimbledon title and then gone on to win the senior singles title?
5 Only two women have performed the feat of winning the junior Wimbledon title and then gone on to win the senior title: Karen Susman is one. Name the other.
6 Whom did Billie Jean King beat 6–0, 6–1, in the 1975 ladies' singles final?
7 Name the two men involved in the first all left-handed men's singles final in 1960?
8 Who was Illie Nastase's partner when he won his first title – the mixed doubles – in 1972?
9 Name either of the two men involved in the longest men's singles final, lasting 58 games?
10 Who was the last mother, before Evonne Cawley in 1980, to win the ladies' singles?

LAWN TENNIS

THE DAVIS CUP

1 Which European country won the 1976 Davis Cup?

2 Who is Great Britain's Davis Cup manager?

3 Which country did the United States beat 3-1 in the 1981 final?

4 Of the Great Britain team which played its opening Davis Cup match in 1981, only one player, apart from Buster Mottram, had previously played in the competition. Name him.

5 Who made his 21st, and record, appearance for Ireland in the Davis Cup when he played against Bjorn Borg in the 1978 competition?

6 Which country did the United States beat in the final of the 1971 Davis Cup – the last time the challenge round system was played? (The following year they beat the same country under the new system.)

7 Great Britain played their first indoor Davis Cup match in 1974, when they played which country at Queens Club?

8 Which man holds the record (164 in all) for appearing in the most Davis Cup matches in a career?

9 . . . and which man has appeared for Great Britain on the most number of occasions?

10 Which country, in 1975, became the first European country since 1936 to win the Davis Cup?

PICTURE QUIZ 2

1 Which Wimbledon final was this? The score gives a clue.

2 Other than Connors, name the three players Borg has beaten in Wimbledon finals.

3 Before 1982, how many Wimbledon singles finals had Connors been in?

4 Whom did Connors beat in his first winning Wimbledon singles final?

5 What was the fourth set tie-break score in the first McEnroe–Borg Wimbledon final?

LAWN TENNIS

WHAT NATIONALITY?

What nationality are the following international tennis stars?

1 Guillermo Villas
2 Diane Fromholtz
3 Vitas Gerulaitis
4 Onny Parun
5 Maria Bueno
6 Manuel Santana
7 Owen Davidson
8 Jan Kodes

FOR THE WOMEN ONLY

The following questions are about tournaments in which only women may compete.

1 Who has appeared in the most number of Wightman Cup ties for Britain?
2 Great Britain won the 1974 Wightman Cup. The match was played in Wales. Where?
3 The first ever professional tournament for women *only* in this country was held at Crystal Palace in 1977. Name the tournament.
4 Who, in 1979, succeeded Roger Taylor as trainer-coach of the British Wightman Cup team?
5 Which American venue staged the inaugural Wightman Cup in 1923?
6 Which country was beaten by the United States in the inaugural Federation Cup in 1963?
7 Great Britain won the 1968 Wightman Cup. Which pair of sisters won the final match to clinch the victory?
8 Who was manager of the British Wightman Cup team, whitewashed 7–0 in 1981?

NICKNAMES

1 Which Wimbledon Champion was nicknamed 'The Rocket'?
2 'Gorgeous Gussie' was the nickname of which postwar player?
3 What nickname was given to the four French stars of the 1920s and 1930s: Borotra, Lacoste, Brugnon and Cochet?
4 'Muscles' was the nickname of an unlucky postwar Wimbledon finalist. Who was he?
5 She won the ladies' singles at Wimbledon on eight occasions and was known as 'Little Miss Poker Face'. Name her.

PICTURE QUIZ 3

1 What is the famous document?
2 In which year did this happen?
3 Why was the list drawn up?
4 Who won Wimbledon's men's singles final that year?
5 . . . and the women's singles?

MODERN PENTATHLON

1 Over what distance is the cross-country running event in the modern pentathlon?
2 . . . and over what distance is the swimming event?
3 Name the other three sports that are contested in the modern pentathlon in addition to the swimming and cross-country running?
4 Name any two of the three Britons who won gold medals at the 1976 Montreal Olympics?
5 Who was the British girl who won the women's World title in 1978?
6 Which country has won the men's team title at the World Championships on most occasions?
7 When Britain won the gold medal in the 1976 Games, which country finished with the silver?
8 Which is the only western country to have produced the Olympic individual champion since the Second World War?
9 Who was the Briton who won the individual title at the Women's World Cup in 1979?
10 Which is the last event of the modern pentathlon?
11 Which major event was won by Danny Nightingale in 1979?

PICTURE QUIZ
Which event is this in the order of modern pentathlon competition?

MOTOR CYCLING

SUPERBIKES

1 Which make of bike did Barry Sheene ride when he won his World title in 1976 and 1977?
2 Mike Hailwood rode an MV Augusta on the four occasions when he won the World 500-cc Championship, but which machine did he ride when winning the World 250- and 350-cc titles?
3 Hailwood came out of retirement to win the Formula One race at the 1978 Isle of Man TT – on which make of bike?
4 Mick Grant switched from the Kawasaki team to which team for the 1979 season?
5 Which works team did dual World Champion Kork Ballington ride for at the time of his winning his World titles?
6 Which team did Geoff Duke leave in 1953 in order to join the Norton team?
7 At the end of the 1973 season, Giacomo Aghostini moved from the MV Augusta team to which works team?
8 In 1960, Derek Minter rode which make of bike to become the first British machine to lap the TT course at over 100 m.p.h.?

FOR THE TRACK RECORD

Questions about tracks.

1 One complete lap is 2.761 miles long, and it is situated near Tarporley in Cheshire. Name it.
2 The Bol d'Or, a famous 24-hour race, is staged on which famous motor-racing circuit?
3 Within a mile either way, how long is the Isle of Man TT course?

MOTOR CYCLING

THE ISLE OF MAN TT COURSE

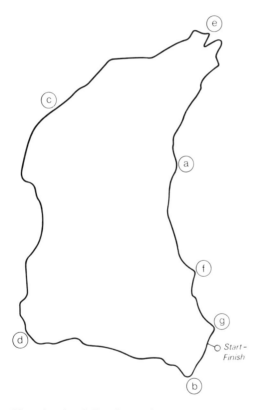

Pinpoint the following points on the Isle of Man TT Course:

1 Ballacraine
2 Ramsey Hairpin
3 Creg-ny-Baa
4 Ballaugh
5 Governors Bridge
6 The Bungalow
7 Quarter Bridge

WHO MAKES THEM?

In which countries are the following bikes manufactured:

1

2

3

4

5

6

MOTOR RACING

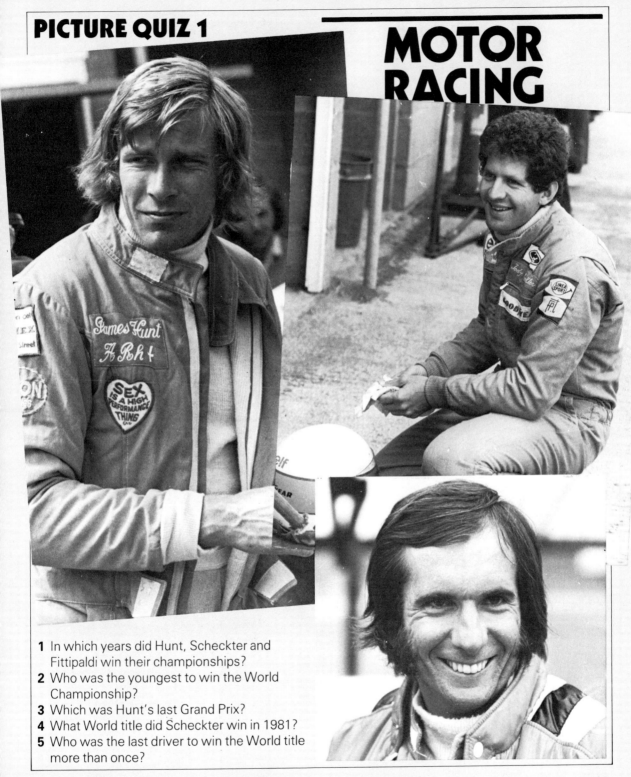

1 In which years did Hunt, Scheckter and Fittipaldi win their championships?
2 Who was the youngest to win the World Championship?
3 Which was Hunt's last Grand Prix?
4 What World title did Scheckter win in 1981?
5 Who was the last driver to win the World title more than once?

MOTOR RACING

GREAT BRITONS

1 Only one driver has won seven Formula One Grand Prix races in a season. He was British. Name him.
2 Who was the first Briton to win the World Championship?
3 Which Briton holds the record (176 altogether) for starting in the most Formula One Grand Prix races?
4 Who was the Briton who won his first Grand Prix – the Austrian – in 1976?
5 Who was the only Englishman to obtain points in the 1981 World Drivers' Championship?
6 British drivers monopolized the World Championship between 1962 and 1965: Graham Hill won in 1962, Jim Clark in 1963 and 1965. Which other Briton won the title in 1964?
7 Which British driver holds the record (27) for the most number of Grand Prix victories in a career?
8 Which Briton is the only man to have won the World Motor-Racing Drivers' title after having been a World Motor-Cycling Champion?

A MIXED BAG FOR THE EXPERT

1 Who was the last man to win at least six Grand Prix races in one season?
2 Who was the first North American to win the World Drivers' title?
3 Following Ronnie Petersen's death at Monza in 1978, the circuit was taken off the Grand Prix list. Which track replaced it as the home of the Italian Grand Prix?

4 Which Formula One driver of 1979 missed most of the season as a result of a hang-gliding accident in which he broke both his legs?
5 Which was James Hunt's last Grand Prix victory in 1977?
6 Who, in 1978, was the first Canadian to win a Formula One Grand Prix?
7 Who was the Swede who won his first Grand Prix in 1977 when he won the Belgian Grand Prix in a Lotus?
8 Which driver, following the death of Ronnie Petersen at Monza in 1978, was sent for trial, charged with his manslaughter?
9 John Watson, driving a Marlbro McLaren, had his second ever Grand Prix success in 1981. His first success was in 1976 when he won the Austrian Grand Prix – in what make of car?
10 Who, in 1981, became the first Swiss driver since Clay Reggazzoni to finish in the first six in a Formula One Grand Prix?
11 Which driver was killed whilst practising for the 1980 German Grand Prix?
12 Which track stages the Jim Clark Memorial Formula Two race?
13 Who is the only man to have won the Indianapolis 500 on *four* occasions?
14 Who was the Briton seriously injured whilst practising for the 1977 British Grand Prix?
15 On which British track can Druids be found?

THE DRIVERS' CHAMPIONSHIP

1 Who was the first man to win the Drivers' Championship two years in succession?
2 Who, in 1963, 1964 and 1965, was the last man to finish runner-up in the Championship three years in succession?
3 When James Hunt won the World title in 1976, two other British drivers obtained points in the final table. Name them.
4 Two United States drivers obtained points in the 1981 World Championship. Mario Andretti was one. Name the other.

5 Jody Scheckter won the 1979 World Championship, but who won the most races in the season?

6 In 1966 and 1967 the winners of the Drivers' Championship both drove Repco Brabhams. The 1966 winner was Brabham himself. Who won the title the following year?

7 He finished second in the Championship in 1951, and in 1952 he won six of the seven Grand Prix races; he later lost his life at Monza. Name him.

8 Ronnie Petersen never won the World title, but he was runner-up on two occasions: posthumously to Mario Andretti in 1978, and also to . . .?

9 In 1958 he won four Grand Prix races yet did *not* win the World title. Name him.

10 Who was the first Austrian to win the World title?

MOTOR RACING

9 What was the first make of car to win the manufacturers' title two years in succession?

10 Mike Hailwood had his last race on four wheels at Nurburgring in 1974 when he crashed. What make of car was he driving at the time?

IDENTIFY THE FOLLOWING CIRCUITS

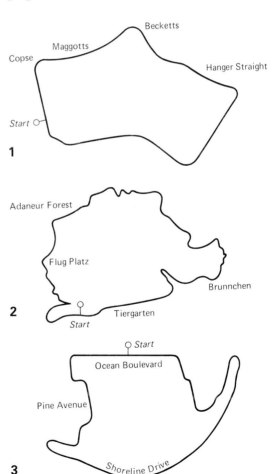

WHAT CAR?

1 Clay Reggazzoni provided which car with its first Grand Prix success when winning the 1979 British Grand Prix?

2 Stirling Moss drove for six manufacturers during his career. Which one provided him with his most Formula One Grand Prix successes (six in all)?

3 What make of car did Jim Clark drive to each of his Grand Prix victories?

4 Who was the first man to win the World Championship driving his own make of car?

5 Jean Pierre Jabouille drove the first ever turbocharged car in 1977 when it made its debut at the British Grand Prix. What make was it?

6 For whom did James Hunt drive in his final season?

7 Jackie Stewart won the World Drivers' Championship three times: twice in a Tyrell Ford, and once in what other make of car?

8 Fangio won the French, Italian and German Grand Prix races in 1954 – in what car?

MOTOR RACING

RALLYING

PICTURE QUIZ 2

You get ten out of ten if you know who the ballerina is – and no bonus points for guessing Graham Hill! Let's look at Hill's career

1 On how many occasions did he win the World drivers' title?
2 He won the Le Mans 24 Hours in 1972 – with which co-driver?
3 What race did he win in 1966 in a red ball at an average speed of 144.32 m.p.h.?
4 How many times did he win the British Grand Prix?
5 Which Grand Prix did he win on five occasions?

1 Who was the last Briton, in 1976, to win the RAC Rally?
2 Which England international footballer partnered Tony Fall in the 1970 World Cup Rally?
3 Who was the last man to win the Monte Carlo Rally three years in succession?
4 In which country is the Rally of a Thousand Lakes staged?
5 Jackie Ickx and Britain's Derek Bell won the 1981 Le Mans Twenty-Four Hour Race. In what make of car?
6 The RAC Rally was first recognized as an official event in 1951, and was won by Ian Appleyard. In what make of car?
7 Who was the Swede, later to marry Stirling Moss's sister, who won the RAC Rally in 1960, 1961 and 1962?
8 Who are sponsors of the RAC Rally?
9 Who was the Irishman who won the 1964 Monte Carlo Rally in a Mini Cooper?
10 In which country is rallying the national sport?
11 How many days did the 1982 Rally last?
12 Who, in 1978, became the first driver to win both the Monte Carlo Rally and the Safari Rally in the same year?
13 Who has won the Safari Rally in 1979, 1980 and 1981?
14 Who was the last Briton, in 1968, to drive to success in the Monte Carlo Rally?
15 Why was there a controversial start to the 1981 Safari Rally?
16 In which city did the 1981 RAC Rally start and finish?

ROWING

1 What is the principal difference between rowing and sculling?
2 Who was the girl who made history by becoming the first female cox of a Boat Race crew in 1981?
3 The losers in the opening races in a competition are allowed to race again for the opportunity to qualify for the finals. What are these races called?
4 What is the name given to the Cambridge University reserve crew?
5 What is the distance of the Boat Race?
6 The 1975 World Championships were held in England – whereabouts?
7 Name six of the eight Olympic rowing categories?
8 Name either of the two men who were the first Britons to win a World title when they won the double sculls in 1977.
9 Which person – associated with royalty – was cox to the Cambridge side that won the 1950 Boat Race?
10 What is the minimum weight of a cox in a senior race?

PICTURE QUIZ

1 Name the course?
2 Which Blue Riband race is this?
3 Name the other Blue Riband race at the same course?
4 In 1979, which British crew won the race pictured here?
5 This is the 1975 race – who were the winners?

RUGBY LEAGUE

A MIXED BAG

1 Who made his 500th appearance for Leeds during the 1981–82 season?
2 Which club finished eighth in the Championship in 1973, yet went on to win the Championship play-off final by beating Leeds?
3 Which side used to play its home matches at Parkside?
4 Hull KR established a new transfer record in 1980 when they bought Len Casey from Bradford Northern for £35,000. They held the previous record at the time – £30,000 – paid for which player in 1979?
5 Who, in 1956–57 season, set a record for a United Kingdom player by scoring 60 tries in a season?
6 Who is the only man to have been sent off in a Challenge Cup Final at Wembley?
7 McDonald Bailey, the international sprinter, played professional Rugby League – all be it just one game. Which club did he play for?
8 Who was the first player to move from Fulham to Cardiff?
9 Which team did Wigan beat in the first Challenge Cup Final at Wembley in 1929?
10 Which was the first club to install undersoil heating at its ground?
11 Who was the Widnes player who beat the 58-year-old record in 1981 when he played his 191st consecutive match?
12 Which player, in 1973, was involved in the first £20,000 transfer?
13 . . . and which player, in 1981, was involved in the first £50,000 transfer?
14 Three soccer grounds have been used to stage the championship play-off final: Elland Road and Maine Road are two. Name the third.

WHERE DO THEY PLAY?

Match up each league club with its correct home ground.

1 Castleford	(a) Tatters Field
2 Featherstone R	(b) Naughton Park
3 St Helens	(c) Post Office Road
4 Batley	(d) Whieldon Road
5 Doncaster	(e) Alt Park
6 Halifax	(f) Knowsley Road
7 Huyton	(g) Wilderspool
8 Warrington	(h) Central Park
9 Widnes	(i) Mount Pleasant
10 Wigan	(j) Thrum Hall

LANCE TODD WINNERS

For which clubs did the following men play at the time of their winning the Lance Todd Award for being the Man of the Match in the Challenge Cup Final?

1 1980, Brian Lockwood
2 1971, Alex Murphy
3 1950, Gerry Helme
4 1975, Ray Dutton
5 1969, Malcolm Reilly
6 1956, Alan Prescott

NICKNAMES

Match up the clubs with their correct nicknames.

1 Villagers	(a) Leeds
2 Airlie Birds	(b) Swinton
3 Gallant Youths	(c) Bramley
4 Loiners	(d) Warrington
5 Roughyeds	(e) Castleford
6 Lions	(f) Wakefield
7 Glassblowers	(g) Hull KR
8 Dreadnoughts	(h) Batley
9 Robins	(i) Oldham
10 Wires	(j) Hull

PICTURE QUIZ 1

1 A Widnes fan defying police and gravity at the 1975 Challenge Cup Final when Widnes beat the holders. Who were the holders?
2 Widnes lost in the Challenge Cup Final the next year. Who beat them?
3 And who was the winning captain in the 1976 final?
4 Widnes won the Challenge Cup in 1979 beating which team in the final?
5 How many Challenge Cup Finals have Widnes played, since and including 1975?

RUGBY LEAGUE

THE CHALLENGE CUP

1 They appeared in the very first Challenge Cup Final in 1897, but had to wait until 1956 for their first ever win in the final. Name them.

2 Huddersfield hold the record for the highest score in the Challenge Cup, when they scored 119 points against which side in 1914?

3 Which club holds the record for the most appearances in the Challenge Cup Final?

4 Which player kicked eight goals for Featherstone Rovers in the 1973 final against Bradford Northern?

5 Which player, in 1960, made his senior debut for his side in the Challenge Cup Final against Wakefield Trinity?

6 Which man appeared in the 1952 final whilst over the age of 40 – the only man over this age to have appeared in a final?

7 The last time any team scored over 60 points in a match in the Challenge Cup was in 1973 when Leigh scored 64 points against which non-league team?

8 Since 1929, when the first Challenge Cup Final was played at Wembley, only two teams have played in the final and never lost. Name them both.

9 Only three teams have failed to score in a Challenge Cup Final at Wembley, and ironically it happened in three successive years – 1949, 1950 and 1951. Name any two of the three teams to fail to score?

10 Which non-league team was beaten 23–22 by the powerful Castleford side in the first round of the Challenge Cup in 1977–78?

1 What is the stadium?
2 To the nearest thousand, what is the record attendance?
3 In which match was the record set?
4 Who won the match?

THE PREMIERSHIP TROPHY

1 The Premiership Trophy was first introduced in 1975. Which club appeared in each of the first three finals?
2 Which ground staged the Premiership Trophy final in the three successive years between 1976 and 1978?
3 Which player in 1979 established a record by scoring eight goals, the most in any one match in the Premiership Trophy?
4 Which is the only club to have won the Premiership Trophy final, and also staged a Premiership Trophy final?
5 Which player holds the record for scoring the most points in a Premiership final – 17 in 1977?

PICTURE QUIZ 1

1 Which club did Gareth Edwards play for?
2 How many consecutive games did he play for Wales?
3 How many tries did he score for Wales?
4 Who succeeded him as the most capped Welshman?
5 Who first succeeded him as Wales's scrum half?

RUGBY UNION

CAP THAT: POSTWAR INTERNATIONALS

1 For which club side does England full-back Dusty Hare play?
2 Who is Wales's most capped player?
3 Who holds the record for scoring the most points in an international career?
4 Which full-back made 19 appearances for England between 1968 and 1972?
5 Who has captained England on the greatest number of occasions?

6 For which club side does Scottish international Andy Irvine play?
7 For which club side did former England international Dickie Jeeps play?
8 Who, in 1979, broke Willie John McBride's world record, when he represented his country, and the British Lions, for the 81st time?
9 Who was the New Zealander who won 55 caps between 1957 and 1971?
10 Who has made the most appearances as full-back for Ireland in international matches?

PICTURE QUIZ 2

Name these famous All Blacks.

A MIXED BAG

1 Who captained England on their first ever tour to Australia in 1972?

2 How long did France have to wait before they won the Five Nations title outright?

3 Who scored 35 of the British Lions 38 Test Match points in the 1968 series with South Africa?

4 Paul Ringer of Wales was sent off in the 1980 international against England at Twickenham, following a late tackle on whom?

5 Which club won the French Club Championship six times in the 1970s?

6 Who scored two tries for the Northern Division in their memorable victory over the 1979 All Blacks?

7 . . . and who captained the Northern Division that day?

8 The Barbarians had their biggest ever win in 1978. Which team did they beat 84–12?

9 Scotland had three captains during the 1979–80 season: Ian McLauchlan and Andy Irvine were two. Name the third.

10 Which was the last county, before Gloucestershire, to win the County Championship three years in succession?

11 Who was the leading points scorer for the British Lions on their 1977 tour to New Zealand?

12 Which member of the England squad in 1981 made his international debut in 1974 whilst playing for Nottingham?

13 Two first-class English sides have letters on their shirts instead of numbers. Leicester is one. Name the other.

14 Who scored 37 points for the Lions in their match against South West Districts on their 1974 tour of South Africa?

15 For which Irish team did former Welsh hero Cliff Morgan play?

THE CLUB TOURNAMENTS

1 Who captained Gosforth in the absence of Roger Uttley when they won the John Player Cup for the first time in 1976?

2 Who was the Rosslyn Park forward who was dismissed from the field for violent play during the final of the 1975–76 John Player Cup?

3 Which club appeared in each of the first five Welsh Cup Finals?

4 Which club was banned from taking part in the 1979–80 John Player Cup following a Rugby Football Union investigation in 1979?

5 Which club, in 1979, became the first to beat Gosforth at Gosforth in the John Player Cup?

RUGBY UNION

6 Which club won the Charrington International Festival at Wembley Stadium at the start of the 1979–80 season?

7 Which club did Gloucester beat 17–6 in the first John Player Cup Final in 1972?

8 Which was the last team to beat Leicester in the John Player Cup?

9 Which side beat Bridgend 14–6 to win the Welsh Cup Final in 1981?

10 Which team won the Scottish Championship for the second successive year in 1981?

PICTURE QUIZ 3

1 A couple of England's lesser known internationals. Who are they?

2 Name their clubs.

3 One went to rugby league – to which club?

RUGBY UNION

PICTURE QUIZ 4

1 Who is the player with the ball?
2 What is his nickname?
3 What was his club?
4 Who is following him onto the pitch?
5 On which Lions tours were they team-mates?

PICTURE QUIZ 5

The Welsh Grand Slam team of 1976 – how many of them can you name?

REMEMBER THAT?

1 Which is the largest Rugby Union ground in the world?

2 Who scored 19 points for Wales in his international debut against England in 1967?

3 Which county won the County Championship in each of the first three years after the last war?

4 Which Irish side was the only team to defeat the 1978–79 touring All Blacks?

5 Who was the referee who sent off Geoff Wheel and Willie Duggan in the 1977 Wales–Ireland international?

6 Which club side plays its home matches at McCracken Park, Newcastle?

7 Edgehall Park is the home of which northern team?

8 Which county cricketer scored 19 points for Cambridge in the 1975 Varsity match?

9 Cyril Brownlie of New Zealand was the first man to be sent off in an international. Which other New Zealander was the second to suffer this fate?

10 Where did France play most of their international matches until 1972, when they moved to their present home?

11 Which London side plays its home matches at the Stoop Memorial Ground?

12 Which Rugby Union team was founded by Percy Carpmael in Bradford in 1890?

13 Which man scored 18 of the British Lions' 22 points in the opening Test against South Africa in 1980 – a record for a Lions player?

14 Which side does All Black captain Graham Mourie play for?

15 When Mike Burton became the first Englishman to be sent off in an international, which country was England playing at the time?

SHOOTING

A MIXED BAG

1 Name five of the seven types of shooting for which gold medals were awarded at the 1980 Moscow Olympics.

2 Which Briton won the 1968 clay pigeon shooting Olympic gold medal, with an unprecedented run of 189 consecutive hits out of his total of 198?

3 Which member of the British peerage won a gold medal in the .303 rifle shooting at the 1966 Commonwealth Games?

4 How many points are scored for a bull in rifle and pistol-shooting competitions?

5 What is the other name for clay-pigeon shooting?

6 . . . and how many shots does each competitor have in a clay-pigeon shooting competition?

7 Over what distance, in metres, does a contest shoot in a pistol-shooting event?

8 Which winter Olympic sport features shooting in the programme?

9 Why was Ho Jun Li ticked off by his government after winning a gold medal in the 1972 Olympic Games?

SHOOTING WITH A DIFFERENCE

Sports fans are normally good at remembering film roles; try these few questions on films and guns . . .

1 Who won the Oscar in 1969 for his role in *True Grit*?

2 Which film was voted best film of 1970 by the British Film Academy?

3 Which film won the British Academy's Film of the Year Oscar in 1967?

4 Which film scooped all the American awards in 1969?

5 Who refused the American Oscar in 1970 for his role in *Patton*?

SHOW JUMPING

NATIONALITIES

Give the nationalities of the following show-jumping personalities.

1 Alwin Schockemohle
2 David Broome
3 Bill Steinkraus
4 Raimondo d'Inzeo
5 Nelson Pessoa
6 Eddie Macken

MIX AND MATCH 1

Match up the show jumpers with the horses on which they won the World Championship.

1 Hans Winkler   (a) Beethoven
2 David Broome   (b) Simona
3 Raimondo d'Inzeo   (c) Halla
4 Marion Coakes   (d) Gowran Girl
5 Hartwig Steenken   (e) Stroller
6 Gerd Wiltfang   (f) Rocket
7 Janou Tissot   (g) Roman
   (*née* Lefebvre)

MIX AND MATCH 2

Below are the names of famous riders and the horses they ride. Can you pair them off?

1 David Broome   (a) Mattie Brown
2 Alwin Schockemohle   (b) Merely a Monarch
3 Liz Edgar   (c) Philco
4 Annelli Drummond-Hay   (d) Rex the Robber
5 Paddy McMahon   (e) Forever
6 Harvey Smith   (f) Psalm
7 Ann Moore   (g) Penwood Forge Mill

PICTURE QUIZ

1 Two of our most distinguished equestrian personalities – David Broome and Caroline Bradley. Name the horses.
2 In which year did this male partnership win the prestigious King George V Gold Cup?
3 And in which year did Miss Bradley win the Queen Elizabeth II Cup on this horse?
4 In which Olympics did David Broome win an Olympic medal?
5 On which horse did Caroline Bradley win the Queen Elizabeth II Gold Cup in 1978?

SKIING

1 Who was the only man to win two gold medals at the 1980 Winter Olympics in the skiing events?
2 Who was the last man, in 1968, to win the Olympic downhill and slalom at the same Olympics?
3 Who were the brother and sister who won the World Cup titles in 1980?
4 Which country won the bronze medal in both the men's and women's slalom events at the 1976 Winter Olympics?
5 Franz Klammer won the gruelling Lauberhorn downhill for the third successive year in 1977. Who was the last man, also an Austrian, to win this event three years in succession?
6 Which man went to the 1980 Winter Olympics as reserve to the Austrian downhill team, but due to a dispute in their camp, made the team and won the gold medal?

PICTURE QUIZ

Who is this skier who came within a hundredth of a second of an Olympic medal?

SKI JUMPING

1 How many jumps does a competitor have in an international ski jumping competition?
2 There are two jumping events at the Winter Olympics – the 90-metres jump, and which other?
3 In what year were two ski jumping competitions first introduced at the Olympics?
4 To what distance of accuracy is a jump measured?
5 What is the maximum number of points each judge may award in a competition?
6 Who was the Austrian who won the 90-metres gold medal at the 1976 Winter Olympics?
7 By what name is the distance between the launching platform and the take off known?
8 Name three of the four centres which make up the Four Hills event at Christmas and the New Year.
9 . . . and of those four hills, which is the only one jumped from an actual hill and not an elevated platform?
10 Jiri Raska won a gold medal in the ski jumping competition at the 1968 Winter Olympics. What was his nationality?

PICTURE QUIZ

Toni Innauer

Jouko Tormanen

What nationalities are these two ski jumpers and which events did they win at the 1980 Olympics?

SNOOKER

THE DAVIS CONNECTION

Questions about Joe, Fred and Steve Davis.

1 In which town were both Joe and Fred born?
2 What award did Joe receive in the Honours list?
3 Who is Steve's very successful manager?
4 Steve's first major win as a professional was in 1980 when he beat Alex Higgins in the final of which tournament?
5 How many times did Joe and Fred meet in the final of the World Professional Snooker Championship?
6 Fred won the World Snooker title from the man who succeeded Joe as champion. Name him.
7 Who were Steve's partners in the winning England team that won the World Team Championship in 1981?

PICTURE QUIZ 1

1 Who are the players?
2 Which two were World Billiards Champions?
3 Who is the only professional snooker player in the photo not to have won either the World Snooker or Billiards title?
4 To whom did Fred Trueman lose his World record for Test wickets?
5 And from whom did the other World Champion in the celebrities team win his World title?

PICTURE QUIZ 2

1 How many World finals has Ray Reardon won?
2 How many World finals has he lost?
3 In between his first and last wins, who won the title twice?

POT LUCK

1 What is the name of the theatre which houses the World Professional Championships each year?
2 Who was the unseeded player who knocked holder Steve Davis out in the first round of the 1982 World Professional Championship?
3 Who was Doug Mountjoy playing when he scored a break of 145 in the 1981 World Championships – the highest ever in the tournament?
4 Who is the youngest person ever to have reached the semifinals of the World Professional Championships?

5 Who, in 1977, was the first winner of the UK Professional Championship, beating Doug Mountjoy in the final?
6 Who was the last Englishman before Steve Davis to win the World title?
7 Name the two men Alex Higgins has beaten in the *final* of the World Professional Championships?
8 Who, in 1980, became the first overseas player to win the Professional World title?
9 Who, in 1980, was the Briton who became the youngest ever winner of the World Amateur Championship?
10 Whom did Terry Griffiths beat in the final when he won the World title in 1979?

SOFTBALL

1 Softball is a smaller version of which other sport?
2 How many players are there in a softball team?
3 In which country did softball originate?
4 How many bases are there in a game of softball?
5 . . . and how far apart are the bases: 40 feet; 60 feet; 80 feet or 100 feet?
6 How many innings are there per team in each game?
7 What is the difference between pitching in softball and pitching in the parent game?
8 What is a softball made of?
9 When softball was first introduced in 1887 it was known as indoor baseball. Between then and now, it has had two other names. Give either.
10 The Men's Softball World Championships were first held in 1966; the Women's World Championships were held the previous year. Were they held in Australia, Canada, Mexico or the United States?

SPEED SKATING

1 Which man won five speed skating gold medals at the 1980 Winter Olympics?
2 What was the nationality of three-times World Champion Ard Schenk?
3 What was the longest distance contested at the 1980 Winter Olympics?
4 In which country does speed skating draw crowds comparable with soccer crowds in other countries?
5 How many skaters take part in each race in international competitions?
6 What are the four distances in men's international competitions?
7 Name either of the two women who, since 1976, have won World speed skating and track cycling medals?

PICTURE QUIZ

500 metres

1500 metres

3000 metres

Eric Heiden dominated the men's events in the 1980 Olympics – but here are the current women's Olympic champions. Who are they?

SPEEDWAY

THE FOREIGN CONNECTION

Give the nationalities of the following postwar World Champions.

1 Barry Briggs
2 Ole Olsen
3 Anders Michanek
4 Ove Fundin
5 Ivan Mauger
6 Peter Craven
7 Jack Young
8 Ronnie Moore
9 Bruce Penhall
10 Freddie Williams

A MIXED BAG

1 Which was the last London team to win the British League before 1982?
2 Which team won the British League in 1977 then disbanded?
3 Who was Bruce Penhall's partner when he won the 1981 World Pairs' title?
4 Which Briton won the World Pairs' title in 1976, 1977 and 1978?
5 Which country won the World team cup for the first time in 1979?
6 Which is the only team to have won the British League three times in succession?
7 Who was the last World Champion before 1982 from the European continent?
8 Who is ITV's speedway commentator?
9 Who was the first New Zealander to win the World title?
10 Who, in 1973, is the only Polish rider to become World Champion?

HOME GROUND

1 The cities of Glasgow, London and Manchester have all had tracks of the same name at some time or other. What was the name?
2 Monmore Green is the home of which Midlands club?
3 They share the Shay with a soccer club. Name them.
4 Where in Britain is the largest indoor speedway circuit in the world?
5 Which team rides at Foxhall Heath?
6 . . . and which team holds its home meetings at the Abbey Stadium?
7 The first ever World Championship final was held in England in 1936 – on which track?
8 Which team is based at Dudley in the West Midlands?

WHICH CLUB DID THEY RIDE FOR?

1 Ila Teromaa in 1978 became the first ever Finn to ride in the World Championship final. Which club side did he ride for at the time?
2 Which club did Barry Briggs first ride for in this country?
3 Which club did Peter Collins ride for at the time of his winning the World title?
4 From which club did Harringay buy Split Waterman?
5 John Boulger, the Australian captain, moved to Leicester in June 1977. From which club?
6 John Louis and Kenny Carter finished second and third in the 1981 British Championship. They both rode for the same club at the time. Which?
7 Which was Ole Olsen's first club in this country?
8 Michael Lee, the winner, and David Jessup, the runner-up in the 1980 World Championship final, both rode for the same club at the time. Which?

SQUASH

1 Which country does Jonah Barrington represent at international level?
2 At which public school was squash first played, in 1850?
3 Who, in 1976, was the first winner of the Women's World Open Individual title

4 What is the width of a squash court?
5 Which man won the British Open in 1980 for a record-equalling seventh time?
6 What is the height on a squash court between the cut line and the front wall line?
7 How many points does a game normally go up to?
8 In England, balls are manufactured to give different speeds. How many different speeds are there?
9 Who has won the women's title at the British Open in 1980, 1981 and 1982?

PICTURE QUIZ

1 Identify the player holding the cup and the two in action?
2 How many times was each player British Open Champion?
3 In which years were they World Champions?
4 Where is the British Open now held?
5 For how many consecutive years, including 1982, have Australia won the women's singles at the British Open?

SWIMMING & DIVING

PICTURE QUIZ

1 Name the four.
2 How many Olympic gold medals have they won in total?
3 At which Olympics did the girl win her Olympic golds?
4 The male without the moustache set a record when he won how many national titles at the same championships?
5 How many Olympic medals did the well-known British swimmer win?

SWIMMING & DIVING

BRITISH OLYMPIC MEDALLISTS

1 Who won Britain's only swimming medal at the Mexico Olympics in 1968?

2 Who was the first British woman to win an individual Olympic gold medal?

3 Judy Grinham won the Olympic 100-metres backstroke title in 1956. Which other British girl won the bronze?

4 Great Britain won bronze medals in both the men's and women's diving events at the 1960 Rome Olympics. Brian Phelps won the men's bronze. Who was the girl who also won a bronze?

5 Which man won a silver medal in the 100-metres freestyle at the 1964 Games?

6 British girls won the silver medal in the 4 × 100 metres medley relay at the 1980 Moscow games. Margaret Kelly, June Croft and Anne Osgerby were three of the four members of the squad. Name the fourth.

7 Which British girl won two medals at the 1960 Rome Olympics?

8 Who is the only Briton to have won two individual gold medals in swimming events?

9 Which swimmer won Britain's first medal of the 1980 Moscow Olympics?

10 Which girl won Britain's only swimming medal at the 1948 Games in London?

A MIXED BAG

1 At the 1976 Olympics, Britain had two finalists in the men's 100-metres breaststroke – David Wilkie, and who else?

2 Who was the American Olympic gold medallist who later found fame playing the part of Tarzan on the silver screen?

3 Britain only won one swimming gold medal at the 1960 Rome Olympics. Which girl won it for us?

4 Who was the man who won a bronze medal in the high-board diving event at the 1960 Olympics?

5 How many gold medals did Mark Spitz win in his Olympic career?

6 Which woman holds the record (eight) for winning the most Olympic medals?

7 For which club does Margaret Kelly swim?

8 What nationality is former record-holder Karen Muir – the youngest person ever to have set a world record in any major sport?

9 At which discipline did Rica Reinich win both available gold medals at the 1980 Olympics?

10 Who is the only Briton to win a gold medal in the history of the World Championships?

WHO . . . ?

1 Who was the only Briton to win a medal at the 1982 World Championships?

2 Who, in 1978, was the last swimmer to win the prestigious *Daily Express* Sportswoman of the Year trophy!

3 Who took over from David Wilkie as Olympic 200-metres breaststroke champion?

4 Who was the only non-Iron Curtain swimmer to win a gold medal in the women's events at the 1980 Olympics?

5 Who took David Wilkie's 200 metres breaststroke World record from him in 1982?

6 Who is the only swimmer to have broken 50 seconds for the 100-metres freestyle at the Olympic Games?

TEN-PIN BOWLING

1 What is the maximum score that can be obtained in one game of ten-pin bowling?
2 What is the length of a lane in ten-pin bowling – from the throw line to the first pin?
3 Which British girl won the World Championships in 1981?
4 What is the expression used when one obtains three successive strikes?
5 What is a spare?
6 Which United States President was a regular bowler on the lanes at the White House?
7 What is the maximum weight of a ball?
8 What are the shallow grooves on either side of the lanes called?
9 What is the height of a pin?
10 If a bowler knocks down all ten pins with his first ball, and seven pins with his second and third balls, how many points will he have scored at the end of those first two rolls?

WATER POLO

1 What is the minimum depth of the water in a water polo match?
2 What is the width of the goals?
3 There are seven officials in a water polo match. What are they?
4 A game of water polo has four quarters – lasting how long each?
5 How many players in a water polo team?
6 Water polo was included in the Olympic programme for the first time in 1900, Britain won that first gold medal, but were not represented by a national side. They were represented by a club side. From which city?
7 What was the significance of the water polo match at Kensington Baths on 28 July 1890?
8 Which country has won the Olympic title on the greatest number of occasions?
9 Which country won the gold, silver and bronze medals at the 1904 Olympic Games?
10 Which was the last non-Iron Curtain country – in 1960 – to win the Olympic water polo title?

TRAMPOLINE

1 In which country did trampolining begin?
2 Who, in 1972, was the first Briton ever to win a World title?
3 What is the length of the 'bed' (i.e. the jumping surface, not the actual trampoline)?
4 There are two forms of trampolining: individual competition, and what other?
5 How often are the World Championships contested?
6 How many contacts does a competitor make with the bed during his routine in a competition excluding warm-up?
7 How many judges are there in a competition?
8 Who was the Briton who was World Individual Champion in 1980?
9 Which woman won the first five World titles?

WATER SKIING

1 Two British males won gold medals at the 1981 World Championships. Name them.
2 One of those two was the overall World Champion in 1977. Which one?
3 Which British girl broke the women's world water ski jumping record in 1981?
4 What is the maximum length of the tow rope between the boat and the skier?
5 In which country did water skiing originate?
6 Which actress appeared in the film *Easy to Love* in 1955, to promote water skiing in the same way as Sonja Henie promoted ice skating?
7 At which northern seaside resort was water skiing first recorded in England in 1936?
8 Name any three of the six forms of skiing.

YACHTING

1 What was the name of the yacht in which Francis Chichester sailed to victory in the inaugural Singlehanded Transatlantic Yacht race in 1960?
2 Who, in 1976, was the Frenchman, in *Penduick VI*, who won the Singlehanded Transatlantic race?
3 Yachting's premier competition, it was first contested in 1870 and has been won by the United States every year since. Name it.
4 Name three of the four main international classes.
5 Initially it was known as the One Hundred Guinea Cup, but by what name is this famous yachting trophy known today?
6 Which yacht won the 1980 America's Cup?
7 Which European king won a gold medal in the yachting events at the 1964 Olympics?
8 In which country is the oldest yacht club in the world, founded in 1720?
9 What is the letter on the sail which indicates that the boat is British in competitive sailing?
10 Which famous resort staged the yachting events of the 1968 Mexico Olympics?

PICTURE QUIZ

Rodney Pattison winning a gold medal, but . . .
1 In which year?
2 At which centre?
3 With which crewman?
4 With which other crewman did Pattison win a gold medal?
5 In which class of yacht?

YOU NAME IT

AMATEUR AND PROFESSIONAL WRESTLING

1 What is the main difference between freestyle wrestling and Greco-Roman style wrestling?
2 Who is the only Briton to have won a postwar Olympic wrestling medal?

Below is a list of 1982 professional British champions. At which weight are they champions?

1 Tony St Clair	(a) Lightweight
2 Marty Jones	(b) Middleweight
3 Alan Kilby	(c) Heavyweight
4 Brian Maxine	(d) Welterweight
5 Alan Dennison	(e) Light heavyweight
6 Steve Gray	(f) Heavy middleweight

AMERICAN FOOTBALL

Match up each team with the town from which they hail.

1 Pittsburgh	(a) Jets
2 Buffalo	(b) Raiders
3 New York	(c) Packers
4 Green Bay	(d) Bills
5 Oakland	(e) Steelers

BASEBALL

Match up each club with the town from which it hails.

1 Pittsburgh	(a) Yankees
2 Boston	(b) Cardinals
3 Los Angeles	(c) Athletics ·
4 New York	(d) Pirates
5 St Louis	(e) Reds
6 Oakland	(f) Red Sox
7 Cincinatti	(g) Dodgers

BASKETBALL The National Basketball League

1 Which First Division team plays its home matches at the Aston Villa Centre?
2 Ovaltine are the sponsors of which team?
3 Which British league team finished runners-up to Tel Aviv Maccabi in the 1982 World Club Championship?
4 Which team lost their first home match in over six years in 1981, narrowly losing 95–93?
5 Who was voted Britain's most valuable player for the second successive year in 1981?
6 Which men's team play their home matches at Warrington?
7 Who were the 1981 National Cup winners, beating Doncaster in the final?

CROSS-COUNTRY RUNNING The World Championships

1 Which Irishman won the World title in 1978 and 1979?
2 Which race course staged the 1979 race?
3 What nationality is Grete Waitz, winner of the Ladies' World Championship?
4 Who, in 1971, was the last Englishman to win the World title?
5 A Belgian, he won the World Championship four times between 1962 and 1972. Name him.
6 Which is the only Iron Curtain country to have won the World team title?
7 Which is the only other English-speaking country to have won the World men's team title besides England?
8 Who won the World cross-country title and an Olympic gold medal in 1968?
9 Who is the only American male to have won the World cross-country title?

CYCLING PICTURE QUIZ

1 Which resort is the tour leaving?
2 If the car is new – what year is it?

3 . . . and which Dutchman won?
4 Which Briton won the race in 1965 and 1967?

CYCLING
The Tour de France

1 Who was the last man to have won the Tour de France without ever having won the leader's yellow jersey?
2 Who was the Irishman who wore the yellow jersey in the 1963 Tour?
3 Which man won eight stages in the 1976 race, yet he never won the race?
4 The 1974 Tour came to Britain for a special stage. Where was it held?
5 Who was the Frenchman who won the 1975 race?

6 Who was the Briton who won a stage in the 1959 race by an incredible margin of 20 minutes 6 seconds?
7 Who was the Frenchman who, in 1955, became the first man to win the race three years in succession?
8 Two men have won the Tour on five occasions. Name them.
9 In which country did the 1982 Tour de France start?
10 Tommy Simpson died on the unlucky 13th stage of the 1967 Tour. The following day all the riders let which Briton ride through to take the 14th stage in memory of Simpson?

ODDS 'N' ENDS

1 Frisbee throwing has seen many different forms, but what new frisbee competition was introduced at Irvine, California, in 1981?
2 Dressage is the elegant section of the equestrian world. What does dressage mean?
3 What is the difference between a toboggan and a luge?
4 What do surfers call the cascade of white surf upon which they so much depend?
5 Name the three forms of roller skating used in competitions?
6 What is the length of a drag-racing strip from the starting line to the finishing line?
7 In snooker and billiards it is called the screw shot. What is it called in pool?
8 Which Briton won the World 500-cc Moto Cross title in 1979?
9 Many times Professional World Cyclo Cross Champion Albert Zweiffel hails from which country?
10 By what other name is harness racing known?
11 Which footballer won the title of Britain's Best Dressed Man in 1980?
12 Which Sportsman was 'Head of the Year' in 1980 – an award given by the National Hairdressers Association?
13 What happened at Cowes on 1 and 2 August 1982?
14 Rear Admiral Woodward led our troops to the Falklands – but what happened to him at Cowes on 4 August 1982?
15 Which sportsman was Pipe-Smoker of the Year in 1974?
16 . . . and in 1977?
17 Who was Journalist of the Year in 1981?

SUMS

Add together the number of players in each of the following teams to arrive at the answers:
1 Outdoor handball + hurling
2 Netball + polo
3 Volleyball + water polo
4 Australian football + Canadian football
5 Ice hockey + Gaelic football

YOU NAME IT

TABLE TENNIS

1 What are the names of the trophies for the men's and women's teams at the World Championships?
2 Who was the Briton who won the men's European title in 1980?
3 Who is the only man to have won 21 World titles?
4 Who was the last Briton to win the men's singles at the World Championships?
5 A former Wimbledon tennis champion, she was runner-up in the 1956 and 1957 World Table Tennis Championships. Name her.

THREE-DAY EVENTING

1 On which horse did Princess Anne gain her individual gold medal at the 1971 European Championships?
2 . . . and on which horse did she compete in the 1976 Montreal Olympics?
3 She was the first woman to appear in a gold-medal-winning team at the Olympics, and is now known as Jane Holderness-Roddam. By what name was she known at the time of her Olympic success?
4 Lucinda Prior Palmer has won Badminton on four occasions. Name any two of the four horses she has ridden to success in the tournament.
5 Princess Anne and Lucinda Prior Palmer were two of the four members of the British Three-Day-Event team at the Montreal Olympics. Name either of the other two.
6 Who rode Great Ovation to win the Badminton Horse Trials in 1971 and 1972?
7 Jane Holderness-Roddam won the Badminton Three-Day Event on Our Nobby in 1968. She also won the event ten years later, but on which horse?

YOU NAME IT

WEIGHTLIFTING

1 What are the two types of style adopted in international weightlifting?
2 Which country did Precious McKenzie represent at the 1978 Commonwealth Games?
3 Who was the Russian who won the super-heavyweight class at the Montreal Olympics?

PICTURE QUIZ

1 Who is this character?
2 At which Olympics did he win gold medals?
3 What is his hobby?
4 Who took over from him as Olympic champion?
5 What is his weight category in kilos?

WOULD YOU BELIEVE IT?

1 Which former ITV newsreader's father was responsible for giving the googly to cricket?
2 Mike Brearley, in 1979, became the first English captain since W. G. Grace in 1896 to take what on tour of Australia?
3 Which popular singer of the 1950s and 1960s was at one time the pitcher for the Houston Buffaloes baseball team?
4 James Hunt, in 1977, finished fourth in what unofficial world championship at a speed of just seven miles per hour?
5 Which former World athletics record-holder played the part of the gay American footballer in the ITV series 'Soap'?
6 Why did Geoff Boycott leave the field on the fourth day (Sunday) of the first Test against Australia at Trent Bridge in 1981 when all the other players remained on the field?
7 Which English racecourse is owned by Mr Muddle?
8 Name either of the two men who contested the final of the Wormwood Scrubs Chess Tournament in 1977.
9 Which World Championship did Michael Fordham win at Witcham, Cambridgeshire, in 1981?
10 Which golfer celebrated his first win in three years in 1981 by diving fully clothed into a pond?
11 1982 Yugoslav champions, Dynamo Zagreb, were without opposition in a 1981–82 league match in October. Why?
12 What is Octapush?
13 What unique feat did brother and sister Alistair and Janet Bell achieve at Sidmouth in 1981?
14 With what sport would you associate Marco Polo?
15 When No. 5 goes into bat, how many wickets are there still to fall in a cricket match?
16 How did boxer Maurice Hope celebrate the day after losing his World boxing title?

ANSWERS

ASSOCIATION FOOTBALL

A Mixed Bag

1 Plymouth Argyle
2 Bert Trautmann
3 Gerry Hitchens
4 Scotland
5 Joe Mercer
6 Ted Croker
7 The Wanderers
8 Huddersfield Town
9 Arsenal
10 FC Cologne
11 Nat Lofthouse (3)
12 Nottingham Forest
13 Martin Peters
14 Manchester United
15 Ray Kennedy
16 Port Vale
17 Nobby Stiles
18 Jim Blyth (Coventry City)
19 Trevor Cherry
20 Northern Ireland
21 Josef Masopust
22 Leicester City
23 Raymond Kopa
24 Jairzinho
25 Geoff Bradford

Which Country?

1 (e)
2 (d) or (a)
3 (a) or (d)
4 (f)
5 (h)
6 (j)
7 (i)
8 (b)
9 (g)
10 (c)

Picture Quiz 1

From left: *Back row* – Harold Shepherdson (trainer), Martin Peters (Tottenham Hotspur), Peter Storey (Arsenal), Martin Dobson (Burnley), Trevor Brooking (West Ham), Dave Watson (Sunderland), Alan Stevenson (Burnley), Phil Parkes (Queen's Park Rangers), Malcolm Macdonald (Newcastle) and Sir Alf Ramsey. *Front row* – Stan Bowles (Queen's Park Rangers), Mike Channon (Southampton), Colin Todd (Derby), David Nish (Derby), Duncan McKenzie (Nottingham Forest) and Kevin Beattie (Ipswich)

The 500 Club

1 Mike Summerbee
2 Derek Dougan
3 Danny Blanchflower
4 Geoff Hurst
5 Frank Large
6 Stan Anderson
7 George Eastham
8 Billy Meredith
9 Frank McLintock
10 Gordon Banks

Picture Quiz 2

1 *From left*: Mervyn Day (then West Ham), Colin Todd (then Derby) and Denis Law
2 1975
3 Norman Hunter
4 Kevin Beattie
5 Andy Gray

New to the League

1 Cambridge United
2 Colchester United; Gillingham; Scunthorpe United; Shrewsbury Town
3 Wimbledon
4 Peterborough United
5 Newport County
6 Ipswich Town

So You Think You Know the FA Cup?

1 Mick Martin (WBA)
2 Harry Dowd
3 Johnny Dixon
4 Ernie Taylor
5 Manchester United (1957 and 1958)
6 Roy Dwight (Elton John's uncle)
7 Bobby Stokes
8 Newcastle United (1951 and 1952)
9 Nat Lofthouse
10 Sheffield Wednesday (1896)

A Mixed Bag for the Expert

1 Jim Langley (ex Fulham)
2 Gylmar
3 West Brom
4 Accrington Stanley
5 Jimmy Adamson
6 John Harris (Sheffield United)
7 FC Den Haag
8 Bolivia
9 Newcastle United (1977–78)
10 Kevin Tully
11 West Brom (1954)
12 Jimmy Blair
13 Bobby Charlton (1957 and 1958)
14 Colchester United
15 Ken Aston

Picture Quiz 3

(a) Keith Robson (West Ham)

(b) Lothar Emmerich (West Germany)

(c) Ray Clemence (then Liverpool)

In What Year?

1 1949
2 1955
3 1979
4 1968
5 1964

Picture Quiz 4

1 Barnsley and Bolton Wanderers
2 Oakwell
3 Alan Gowling (Chairman of PFA) far right

Grounds and Nicknames

Bury **3** (j)
Oldham Athletic **6** (a)
Rotherham Utd **9** (h)
Southend United **1** (f)
Everton **10** (d)
Brentford **7** (e)
Luton Town **5** (i)
Lincoln City **4** (c)
Swansea City **8** (b)
Millwall **2** (g)

Name the Clubs

1 Barnsley
2 Stoke City
3 Derby County
4 Bury
5 Bristol City

Fill in the Blanks

(a) 3   (f) 2
(b) Glasgow   (g) Panathanaikos
(c) 5   (h) 0
(d) Benfica   (i) St Etienne
(e) Milan   (j) Rome

Picture Quiz 5

Doncaster Racecourse and Belle Vue, home of Doncaster Rovers

Forward Lines

1 Leicester City (1969)
2 Blackburn Rovers (1960)
3 Leeds United (1965)
4 Preston North End (1964)
5 Liverpool (1950)
6 Southampton (1976)
7 Sheffield Wednesday (1966)
8 Luton Town (1959)

The World Cup

1 Sandor Koscics (Hungary – 11)
2 Chile
3 Juste Fontaine (third place play-off, 1958, France v. West Germany)
4 Ernst Wilimowski (Poland v. Brazil, 1938; Brazil won 6–5)
5 Switzerland (lost 7–5 to Austria, 1954)
6 Uruguay
7 Wales (1958)
8 Czechoslovakia (1962)
9 Honduras
10 Martin Peters and Geoff Hurst
11 Hungary (2–1 in 1958)
12 Vittorio Pozzo
13 George Reader (England)
14 Karl Schnellinger and Uwe Seeler
15 Yugoslavia, France and Belgium

Picture Quiz 6

1 Jimmy Hill
2 He took over as linesman when the referee pulled a muscle
3 Highbury (Arsenal v. Liverpool, 1972)

ATHLETICS

Whom Did They Succeed?

1 Alberto Juantorena
2 Jim Ryun
3 John Walker
4 Brendan Foster
5 Ron Clarke
6 Lasse Viren
7 John Aki Bua
8 John Thomas
9 Jesse Owens
10 Christos Papanicolau

What Nationality?

1 Luxembourger
2 Hungarian
3 Ugandan
4 Rumanian
5 Polish
6 Belgian
7 Australian
8 American
9 New Zealander
10 Argentinian

Who Am I?

1 Bronislaw Malinowski
2 Daley Thompson
3 Grete Waitz

Olympic Venues

1 Athens
2 Los Angeles
3 Tokyo (1964)
4 Munich (1972)
5 1948
6 Lake Placid

For the Expert

1 Ainsley Bennett
2 Steve Scott
3 Nadyezhda Chizhova (USSR), shot
4 Cardiff AC
5 Jersey
6 Mike Bull
7 Renate Stecher
8 Peter Snell
9 Lynn Davies (the first three jumpers all had wind-assisted jumps which did not count as records)
10 Christine Tranter
11 Mike Winch
12 Frank Clement

Picture Quiz 1

David Bedford shaved off his beard and cut his hair after failing to win a medal in the 10,000 metres at the 1972 Olympics

Who Was the First?

1 Diane Leather
2 Charles Dumas
3 Iolande Balas
4 Tommie Smith
5 Herb Elliott
6 Ron Clarke
7 Bob Beamon
8 Randy Matson
9 Mary Rand
10 Tamara Press

Picture Quiz 2

1 (a) Abebe Bikila
 (b) Filbert Bayi
 (c) K2 is Kip Keino, K1 is Ben Jipcho
 (d) John Akii-Bua
2 Bikila, Ethiopia; Bayi, Tanzania; Keino and Jipcho, Kenya; Akii-Bua, Uganda

3 1960 and 1964
4 Seb Coe (1500 metres)
5 Two – 1500 in 1968, steeplechase in 1972
6 Steeplechase
7 West Germany
8 Keino, gold in 1972; Jipcho, silver in 1972; Bayi, silver in 1980

World Mile Record

1 Jim Ryun (July 1966 to May 1975)
2 Gunder Haegg
3 Derek Ibbotson
4 Steve Ovett
5 Herb Elliott (1958)
6 Bislet Stadium, Oslo
7 Sydney Wooderson
8 John Walker (1975)
9 Peter Snell
10 Chris Chataway

A Mixed Bag

1 E. McDonald-Bailey
2 Collette Besson
3 Derek Ibbotson
4 Ron Clarke
5 Lynn Davies
6 1500 metres
7 West Indies
8 Howard Payne
9 John Carlos
10 1500 metres
11 Dorothy Hyman
12 The Zatopeks

The Marathons

1 Abebe Bikila (Ethiopia)
2 Alberto Salazar
3 Toshihiko Seko
4 Chris Stewart
5 Joyce Smith
6 Dick Beardsley/Inge Simonssen

In Which Event?

1 800 metres
2 Long jump
3 400 metres hurdles
4 100 metres
5 Discus
6 High jump
7 1500 metres
8 200 metres
9 Shot
10 5000 metres

Rule Britannia

1 Lynn Davies
2 Gordon Pirie
3 Sheila Sherwood
4 Paul Nihill
5 Harold Abrahams
6 Anne Packer
7 Maurice Herriott
8 Martin Reynolds
9 Dorothy Shirley
10 Ken Matthews

BADMINTON

1 5 feet 0 inches
2 Uber Cup
3 Gillian Gilks
4 Rudi Hartono
5 Fleming Delfs
6 Danish
7 Indonesia
8 44 feet
9 16
10 Nora Perry and Jane Webster (1980 women's doubles)

Picture Quiz

Ray Stevens

BIATHLON

1 Russia
2 1960
3 20 kilometres
4 Both. They have four shots at each target – two standing, two prone
5 Four
6 Run a penalty lap of 200 metres
7 Soviet Union
8 Swedish
9 In the relay, competitors fire just one shot standing and one shot prone

BILLIARDS

1 2
2 12 feet
3 Walter Lindrum
4 Rex Williams
5 Mary Queen of Scots
6 Yes. He held it from 1928 to 1933
7 Michael Ferreira
8 Rex Williams
9 1980
10 Norman Dagley

BOB-SLEIGHING

1 Four
2 Robin Dixon and Tony Nash
3 Willie Davenport (100 metres hurdles gold medallist)
4 Front
5 15

6 (a) Italy
  (b) West Germany
  (c) Austria
7 So as to enable him to re-align his sight when coming out of the bend
8 St Moritz (Switzerland)
9 Eugenio Monti of Italy
10 1500 metres
11 Every year
12 Italy (14)
13 Switzerland (12)
14 East Germany (1981)

BOWLS

1 W. G. Grace
2 25 yards
3 Vernon (Vernon Lee beat Glynn Vernon)
4 Arthur Murray
5 David Bryant
6 Blackpool
7 A rink
8 Four
9 Kitty or cot
10 Maldwyn Evans
11 Leonard Trophy
12 Sydney
13 South Africa
14 David Bryant

BOXING

In What Year?

1 (f)
2 (g)
3 (h)
4 (a)
5 (b)
6 (d)
7 (e)
8 (c)

Nicknames

1 John L. Sullivan
2 Jimmy Braddock
3 Nonpareil
4 Billy Aird
5 Rocky Marciano
6 Henry Armstrong
7 Jim Wicks

The Name's the Same

1 Jack Dempsey
2 Baer (Max and Buddy)
3 Gardner (Jack and John L.)
4 Johnson (Marvin and Bunny)
5 Moore (Archie and Davey)

Which Country?

1 Ireland
2 Germany
3 Yugoslavia
4 Ghana
5 Nigeria
6 Brazil
7 Finland
8 Hawaii
9 Scotland
10 England

A Mixed Bag

1 Ingemar Johannson
2 One hour
3 Chris Finnegan
4 Floyd Patterson
5 Terry Lawless
6 Jack Johnson
7 Just once
8 Henry Armstrong
9 George Foreman and Joe Frazier
10 Floyd Patterson

At What Weight?

1 (e)
2 (g)
3 (j)
4 (a)
5 (f)
6 (i)
7 (b)
8 (c)
9 (h)
10 (d)

Picture Quiz 1

1 Muhammad Ali
2 New York
3 1971
4 Round 15
5 Ron Stander (RSF 4)

In Which Round?

1 Round 6
2 Round 3
3 Round 15
4 Round 15 (Draw)
5 Round 10
6 Round 4

So You Think You Know Muhammad Ali?

1 Brian London
2 Floyd Patterson
3 Joe Frazier
4 Zaire (Kinshasa)
5 Ken Norton
6 George Chuvalo
7 Henry Cooper
8 Zora Folley
9 Sonny Liston
10 Highbury Stadium (Arsenal FC)

Who Was It?

1 Henry Cooper
2 Bunny Johnson
3 Dick Turpin
4 Marcel Cerdan
5 Jorge Ahumada
6 Wyatt Earp
7 Rocky Marciano (both hail from Brockton, Mass.)
8 Jack Sharkey
9 Mate Parlov
10 Tommy Farr and Joe Bugner

Venues

1 Havana
2 Copenhagen
3 Las Vegas (Caesars Palace)
4 Copenhagen
5 Lewiston, Maine
6 Manchester
7 Mexico City
8 Munich

Picture Quiz 2

1 Rocky Mattioli (Italy) (Rtd 8)
2 Wilfred Benitez (KO 12)
3 Mike Baker (USA) (RSF 7)
4 Dieter Kottysch (West Germany)
5 Reg Ford (Guyana)
6 Minter won with a second round KO
7 Dave 'Boy' Green and Kirkland Laing; Ford won both
8 Jorge Ahumada (Argentina)
9 Another Argentine, Victor Galindez
10 Alvaro Lopez (RSF 15), Mate Parlov (lost on points), Matthew Saad Muhammad (lost on points in first fight)

Picture Quiz 3

1 Chuck Wepner
2 *Rocky I*
3 Lost in round 15 to Muhammad Ali in March 1975

Picture Quiz 4

1 Jimmy Ellis (USA)
2 Las Vegas, 1973; Kuala Lumpur, 1975
3 Earnie Shavers (USA)
4 Jean Pierre Coopman (Belgium)
5 Frazier won on points over 12 rounds

Rule Britannia

1 Walter McGowan
2 Bob Fitzimmons
3 Terry Downes
4 John H. Stracey
5 Dave 'Boy' Green
6 Carlos Herrera
7 Brian London
8 Don Cockell

British Champions

1 Chris Finnegan
2 Brian Curvis
3 John L. Gardner
4 Terry Downes
5 Larry Paul
6 Don Cockell
7 Dave Charnley
8 Henry Cooper
9 Pat Cowdell
10 Alan Minter

CANOEING & KAYAKING

1 England
2 In canoeing the paddler kneels, and uses a single-bladed paddle; in kayaking the paddler sits, and uses a double-bladed paddle
3 Gert Fredrikson
4 Kayak singles, kayak pairs, kayak fours, Canadian singles, Canadian pairs
5 Canoe polo (you'd think the horses would fall out)
6 Wild water; long-distance and sprint racing
7 Half a mile
8 Seven (Canadian Sevens)
9 Albert Kerr
10 Lake Bala (Wales)
11 Belgrade
12 K4 (10,000 metres)
13 Rudigir Helm (East Germany)
14 Birgit Fischer (East Germany)
15 True
16 1948, 1952, 1956, 1960

CRICKET

Picture Quiz 1

1 Bill Bowes
2 Frank Woolley
3 Wally Hammond

A Mixed Bag

1 Essex
2 Wilf Rhodes
3 New Zealand
4 Robin Jackman
5 Gloucestershire
6 Jack Simmons (Lancs, 1980)
7 Rodney Marsh
8 Don Bradman
9 Lancashire
10 Viv Richards

The Name's the Same

1 Graham and Eddie Barlow
2 Freddie and Alan Brown
3 Bill and John Edrich
4 Jack and Robin Hobbs
5 Brian and Bob Taylor

Initials

1 (c)
2 (d)
3 (g)
4 (h)
5 (a)
6 (b)
7 (j)
8 (f)
9 (e)
10 (i)

Do You Remember the 1981 Season?

1 Durham
2 Viv Richards
3 2
4 Sussex
5 Clive Rice
6 Alan Border
7 Keith Fletcher
8 Richard Hadlee
9 Essex
10 Zaheer Abbas
11 Greg Chappell
12 Dirk Wellham

Picture Quiz 2

1 (a) Viv Richards
  (b) Roy Fredericks
  (c) Albert Padmore
  (d) Deryck Murray
2 Richards, Antigua; Fredericks, Guyana; Padmore, Barbados; Murray, Trinidad
3 Padmore
4 Fredericks (Glamorgan)
5 Derek Taylor (Somerset) playing for MCC
6 Murray
7 1966
8 Padmore and Fredericks
9 Fredericks (7 – now overtaken by Richards)
10 Murray (to David Murray)

Players and Countries

1 (b) C. Hill, played for Australia
2 (c) S. F. Barnes, played for England
3 (c) R. Abel, played for England
4 (b) A. D. Gaekwad, played for India
5 (a) W. M. Darling, played for Australia
6 (b) J. M. Parker, played for New Zealand
7 (c) S. M. Nurse, played for West Indies

How Many?

1 2
2 365
3 45
4 4
5 114
6 18
7 21
8 16

Which Ground?

1 Headingley
2 Antigua (St John's)
3 Swansea/Scarborough
4 Southport
5 Napier
6 Headingley
7 Trent Bridge
8 Bramall Lane, Sheffield
9 Middlesbrough
10 The Oval (owned by the Duchy of Cornwall)

Picture Quiz 3

1 (a) Jim Higgs
   (b) Bob Massie
   (c) Doug Walters
   (d) Gary Gilmour
2 Higgs, Victoria; Massie, Western Australia; Walters, NSW; Gilmour, NSW
3 Gilmour
4 Walters
5 Massie took 16 wickets in the match
6 Higgs
7 Massie
8 Massie (6)
9 Higgs
10 Higgs (66)
11 Massie (31)

A Mixed Bag for the Expert

1 Maurice Tate (1923, 1924 and 1925)
2 Northants
3 Javed Miandad
4 Alec Bedser
5 Dick Motz
6 Roy Fredericks
7 Charlie Hill (Australia, 1904)
8 Frank Chester
9 Russell Endean
10 Greg Chappell (Somerset)
11 Graham McKenzie

12 Worcestershire (1972, 1973 and 1974)
13 George Lohmann (Botham took 19 matches)
14 Richard Hutton
15 Denis Compton

So You Think You Know the Gillette Cup?

1 Yorkshire
2 Geoff Boycott (146)
3 Warwickshire
4 Roy Marshall (77 minutes)
5 Asif Iqbal and Norman Gifford
6 Yorkshire (1965)
7 Barry Wood
8 Glenn Turner
9 Hertfordshire
10 Joel Garner (1979)
11 Viv Richards (1979)
12 Don Kenyon
13 Clive Lloyd (1972 and 1975)
14 Arnold Long (57)
15 Geoff Arnold (81)
16 Middlesex (1980)
17 Yorkshire
18 Northants
19 Viv Richards
20 Four (1970, 1971, 1972, 1975)

CURLING

1 Canada
2 Scotland or Holland
3 Bowls
4 Silver Broom
5 A bonspiel
6 Rink
7 40 yards
8 Richmond
9 Canada
10 Norway

Picture Quiz

Sweden

DARTS

1 5 feet 8 inches
2 Steve Brennan
3 Cliff Inglis
4 John Lowe
5 167
6 Alan Glazier
7 Harry Leadbetter
8 St Helens (Windle Labour Club)
9 Maureen Flowers
10 Jocky Wilson
11 Alan Evans (Wales)
12 Jollees Club (Longton, Stoke on Trent)
13 Stefan Lord (twice)
14 Eric Bristow (1980 and 1981)
15 Nicky Virachkul (USA)
16 Alan Evans (1975)
17 Maureen Flowers (1977 and 1979)
18 John Lowe

FENCING

1 Foil, sabre, épée
2 Gillian Sheene
3 Boris Onitshenko
4 The forte is the half of the blade nearest the hand guard and the foible is the other half
5 A bout or assault
6 The area on which the bout takes place
7 Five
8 David Acfield
9 The whole body, including the head
10 Yes – foil and sabre individual only
11 Allan Jay
12 The De Beaumont centre
13 Hungary

Picture Quiz

The men's sabre

GOLF

The British Open

1 Dai Rees
2 Harry Bradshaw
3 Waterloo (Brussels)
4 The 16th
5 Arnauld Massey (France)
6 Bob Charles
7 St Andrews (1939 and 1946)
8 Fred Daly
9 The Parks (Willie Jr, Willie Sr and Mungo)
10 Bobby Locke
11 Twelve
12 Mark James
13 Phil Rodgers (USA)
14 Mike Bonallack
15 John Ball

Picture Quiz 1

1 Old, New, Jubilee and Eden
2 Neil Coles (65)
3 17th
4 Fife
5 He's the resident professional

A Mixed Bag

1 Bob Charles (1963)
2 Nick Faldo
3 Every two years
4 Royal Lytham
5 Sandy Lyle (1980)
6 Dai Rees
7 3 under par
8 Potters Bar
9 Isao Aoki

10 Wentworth
11 Peter Oosterhuis
12 Peter Thomson
13 Troon
14 South African
15 Harry Vardon

On Course

1 Augusta, Georgia
2 Turnberry
3 Hazeltine
4 Swiss
5 Walton Heath
6 Royal Birkdale
7 Prestwick
8 Hoylake

Picture Quiz 2

1 1972
2 1980
3 Canadian Open
4 *Morning Cloud*
5 The famous Sydney–Hobart race

In What Year?

1 (e)
2 (a)
3 (f)
4 (h)
5 (c)
6 (g)
7 (d)
8 (b)

A Mixed Bag for the Expert

1 Tom Watson (1982)
2 Dunlop Masters
3 Peter Oosterhuis (£32,127)
4 Peter and Percy Alliss
5 Tooting Bec Cup

6 Jack Nicklaus (1965 and 1966)
7 Carnoustie
8 Germany (Berlin)
9 Mike Bonallack
10 Liam Higgins
11 Germany
12 Walter Hagen

Picture Quiz 3

1 10 – a record
2 1965
3 1961
4 1976 and 1977
5 World Cup (for Ireland)

GREYHOUND RACING

1 1200 yards
2 Eight (though it is generally five or six in Britain)
3 Black and white stripes
4 White City
5 500
6 Patricia's Hope (1972 and 1973)
7 Wimbledon
8 Birmingham
9 Mick the Miller
10 Belle Vue, Manchester

Picture Quiz

1 Laurie's Panther
2 The Duke of Edinburgh
3 1927
4 Mick the Miller (1929–30)
5 1980

GYMNASTICS

1 Nellie Kim
2 Boris Shaklin
3 Vera Caslavska
4 Elina Mukhina (USSR)
5 Nikolai Andrianov
6 Two
7 Floor exercises

Picture Quiz

1 Valery Borzov, the athletics gold medallist in 1972 in the Sprints
2 Pop singer
3 3 (2 in the team (1972–6), plus combined exercises in 1972)
4 4 (2 in the team (1972–6), beam in 1972, and floor exercises in 1972)
5 Elena Davydova (USSR)

HOCKEY

1 11
2 12 feet
3 India (eight)
4 Zimbabwe
5 Slough
6 100 yards
7 Right inner and left inner
8 Blackheath
9 Zimbabwe (women)
10 Val Robinson
11 35 minutes
12 New Zealand
13 Lincolnshire

Picture Quiz

1 Amsterdam
2 1971
3 Pakistan
4 Teis Kruize
5 India

HORSE RACING

Thanks for the Ride

1 (d)
2 (a)
3 (e)
4 (h)
5 (b)
6 (g)
7 (c)
8 (f)

A Mixed Bag

1 Yves St Martin
2 Cousins
3 Preakness Stakes
4 Fred Archer
5 Lord Killanin (former President of International Olympic Committee)
6 Fred Rimell
7 Prix du Jockey Club
8 Lester Piggott
9 Paul Cook (on 4 July 1981 he rode Princes Gate in the 2.15 at Sandown, Rammanolie in the 5 o'clock at Bath, and Pavilion in the 7.50 at Nottingham)
10 Tom Dreaper
11 16:16, after thirty-two races to 1982

The Grand National

1 Ayala (1963)
2 Bruce Hobbs
3 Royal Mail
4 Dan Moore
5 Freddie
6 Fulke Walwyn
7 Poethlyn
8 William Archer (father of Fred)
9 The Pilgarlic
10 Harry Llewellyn (of show jumping fame)

Play Your Mate

1(a) 2000 Guineas
2(a) Champion Stakes
3(a) Derby
4(a) Benson and Hedges Gold Cup
5(a) 1000 Guineas
6(a) Cambridgeshire
7(a) King George VI Chase
8(a) Prix de L'Arc de Triomphe

1(b) Lincolnshire Handicap
2(b) St Leger
3(b) Grand National
4(b) Chester Cup
5(b) King George VI and Queen Elizabeth II Stakes
6(b) Ebor Handicap
7(b) Cheltenham Gold Cup
8(b) Washington DC International

Picture Quiz 1

1 The first women's race
2 Kempton Park
3 Meriel Tufnell
4 Scorched Earth
5 50 to 1
6 1972 (8 May)

Picture Quiz 2

Sunnyboy providing the Queen Mother with her 300th National Hunt winner at Ascot on 18 February 1976

A Mixed Bag for the Expert

1 Pimlico
2 Asmena
3 Formosa (1868) or Sceptre (1902)
4 Fulke Walwyn (1963–64)
5 Doug Smith
6 Scale of weight for age
7 Light Cavalry (1980 St Leger)
8 Prix de Diane
9 Bill Roycroft
10 It was the first official winner for a female trainer – Nora Willmott
11 J. O. Tobin
12 Tommy Loates
13 Third Earl of Egremont
14 Flying Wild
15 Lorna Vincent

Who Am I?

1 Fred Winter
2 Joe Mercer

Horses for Courses

1 Bogside
2 Thirsk
3 Sedgefield
4 Longchamps
5 Towcester
6 Newcastle
7 Bois de Boulogne (Paris)
8 Market Rasen
9 Wetherby
10 Uttoxeter

Racing Certainties

1 Cambridgeshire
2 14
3 Pat Eddery
4 Foinavon
5 Chester

6 Gordon Richards
7 York
8 Brian Fletcher
9 Brother-in-law
10 Steve Cauthen

Picture Quiz 3

1 Lester Piggott, 1981
2 Joe Mercer, 1979
3 Pat Eddery, 1977

So You Think You Know the Derby?

1 Lester Piggott (Never Say Die, 1954, age 18)
2 Vincent O'Brien
3 Blushing Groom
4 W. R. 'Rae' Johnstone (1948, 1950 and 1956)
5 Craganour
6 Dick Hern (1979 and 1980)
7 Scobie Breasley (1964 and 1966)
8 Lester Piggott (1976 and 1977)
9 Willie Shoemaker
10 Barry Hills (1972, Rheingold; 1978, Hawaiian Sound)

Closed Courses

1 Gatwick
2 Lanark
3 Alexandra Park
4 Cardiff
5 Newport

Identify the Following Courses

(a) Folkestone
(b) Newton Abbot
(c) Chepstow
(d) Yarmouth
(e) Chester
(f) Carlisle

(g) Kelso
(h) Ayr
(i) Beverley
(j) Fakenham

Picture Quiz 4

1 St Leger (Doncaster)
2 1 mile, 6 furlongs, 32 yards
3 Alain Lequeux (1979)
4 Dunfermline (1977)
5 Julio Mariner (1978)

Who Partnered Them?

1 Steve Cauthen
2 Lester Piggott
3 Pat Eddery
4 Tommy Stack
5 Joe Mercer
6 Willie Carson
7 Geoff Lewis
8 Pat Taafe

ICE HOCKEY

A Mixed Bag

1 Six
2 Face off
3 Two
4 20 minutes
5 2 minutes
6 Canada
7 Stanley Cup
8 Dundee Rockets
9 Great Britain (1936)
10 Streatham

Mix and Match

1 (c)
2 (d)
3 (e)
4 (b)
5 (a)

ICE SKATING

Take Your Partners

1 (f)
2 (a)
3 (e)
4 (b)
5 (c)
6 (d)

World and Olympic Champions

1 Robin Cousins
2 Czechoslovakian
3 Alexai Ulanov
4 Jan Hoffman (GDR)
5 Ulrich Salchow (Sweden)
6 Vladimir Kovalev
7 Dorothy Hamill (USA)
8 Ondrej Nepela (1971, 1972 and 1973)
9 Peggy Fleming (1966, 1967 and 1968)

Picture Quiz

1 (a) Alexandr Zaitsev and Irina Rodnina
  (b) Carlo Fassi
  (c) Robin Cousins
  (d) Bernard Ford and Diane Towler
2 Four – from 1966 to 1969
3 Alexai Ulanov (USSR)
4 John Curry
5 Linda Fratianne (USA)
6 Bristol

Great Britons

1 Chris Howarth
2 Janette Altwegg
3 1976
4 Denver
5 Debbie Cottrill

JUDO

1 The Kyu
2 Keith Remfrey and Dave Starbrook
3 Jane Bridge
4 Neil Adams
5 Dutch
6 Heavier (93 kilogrammes or 14 stone 9 pounds)
7 A shiai
8 30 × 30 feet
9 White
10 1964

Picture Quiz 1

1 (a) David Starbrook
  (b) Brian Jacks
2 Jacks won bronze at middleweight in 1972; Starbrook won silver at light heavy in 1972, bronze in 1976
3 Seven

Picture Quiz 2

Yashuro Yamashita

KARATE

1 Four (one in each corner)
2 Great Britain
3 Tamashiwara
4 Great Britain
5 White
6 32 × 32 feet
7 Red Flag, white flag and whistle
8 The team manager, who addresses himself to the controller
9 1970
10 Hit it or kick it. It's a padded board which he uses for practising punching or kicking techniques

LAWN TENNIS

A Mixed Bag

1 Fred Hoyles
2 Andres Gimeno
3 Helen Gourlay
4 Tony Roche
5 John McEnroe (1977)
6 Cliff and Nancy Richey
7 Arthur Ashe
8 Bill Tilden
9 Stade Roland Garros
10 Martina Navratilova
11 Rod Frawley
12 Spencer Gore
13 Ken Rosewall (1971 and 1972)
14 Gene and Sandy Meyer
15 Roy Emerson

Picture Quiz 1

1 1976
2 Dick Stockton

Wimbledon Winners

1 Newcombe and Roche (1968/69/70)
2 Betty Stove
3 Evonne Cawley (1980 v. Mrs Lloyd)
4 Bjorn Borg
5 Anne Jones
6 Evonne Goolagong
7 Neale Fraser and Rod Laver
8 Rosie Casals
9 Drobny and Rosewall (1954)
10 Dorothy Lambert Chambers (1914)

Picture Quiz 2

1 1977
2 Roscoe Tanner, John McEnroe and Ilie Nastase
3 Four – 1974, 1975, 1977 and 1978
4 Ken Rosewall (1974)
5 18–16

The Davis Cup

1 Italy
2 Paul Hutchins
3 Argentine
4 Richard Lewis
5 Michael Hickey
6 Rumania
7 Iran
8 Nikki Pietrangeli
9 Mike Sangster
10 Sweden

What Nationality?

1 Argentinian
2 Australian
3 American
4 New Zealander
5 Brazilian
6 Spanish
7 Australian
8 Czechoslovakian

For the Women Only

1 Virginia Wade
2 Deeside Leisure Centre
3 Bremar Cup
4 David Lloyd
5 Mission Hills
6 Australia
7 Christine and Nell Truman
8 Sue Mappin

Nicknames

1 Rod Laver
2 Gussie Moran
3 The Four Musketeers
4 Ken Rosewall
5 Helen Wills-Moody

Picture Quiz 3

1 The ATP list of withdrawals on the Wimbledon boycott
2 1973
3 Because of a ban on Nikki Pilic
4 Jan Kodes
5 Billie-Jean King

MODERN PENTATHLON

1 4000 metres
2 300 metres
3 Fencing, shooting, cross-country riding
4 Danny Nightingale, Jim Fox, Adrian Parker
5 Wendy Norman
6 USSR
7 Czechoslovakia
8 Sweden
9 Kathy Tayler
10 Cross-country running
11 Spartakiad

Picture Quiz

Second

MOTOR CYCLING

Superbikes

1 Suzuki
2 Honda
3 Ducati
4 Honda
5 Kawasaki
6 Gilera
7 Yamaha
8 Norton

For the Track Record

1 Oulton Park
2 Le Mans
3 37.73 miles

The Isle of Man TT Course

1 (d)
2 (e)
3 (f)
4 (c)
5 (g)
6 (a)
7 (b)

Who Makes Them?

1 Japan
2 England
3 Germany
4 Spain
5 Italy
6 Austria

MOTOR RACING

Picture Quiz 1

1 Hunt, 1976; Fittipaldi, 1972 and 1974; Scheckter, 1979
2 Fittipaldi, twenty-three in 1972
3 Japanese Grand Prix, 1977
4 Superstars
5 Niki Lauda, 1975 and 1977

Great Britons

1 Jim Clark (1963)
2 Mike Hawthorn
3 Graham Hill
4 John Watson
5 Nigel Mansell
6 John Surtees
7 Jackie Stewart
8 John Surtees

A Mixed Bag for the Expert

1 Jim Clark (1963)
2 Phil Hill
3 Imola
4 Patrick Depailler
5 Japanese
6 The late Giles Villeneuve
7 Gunar Niellson
8 Riccardo Patrese
9 Penske
10 Mark Surer
11 Patrick Depailler
12 Hockenheim
13 A. J. Foyt
14 David Purley
15 Brands Hatch

The Drivers' Championship

1 Alberto Ascari
2 Graham Hill
3 Tom Pryce and John Watson
4 Eddie Cheever
5 Alan Jones
6 Denny Hulme
7 Alberto Ascari
8 Jackie Stewart (1971)
9 Stirling Moss
• 10 Jochen Rindt

What Car?

1 Saudi Williams
2 Vanwall
3 Lotus
4 Jack Brabham
5 Renault (Elf RS01)
6 Wolf
7 Matra Ford
8 Mercedes Benz
9 Cooper (1959–60)
10 Surtees

Identify the Following Circuits

1 Silverstone
2 Nurburgring
3 Long Beach

Picture Quiz 2

1 Two
2 Henri Pescarolo
3 Indianapolis 500
4 Never
5 Monaco

RALLYING

1 Roger Clark
2 Jimmy Greaves
3 Sandro Munari (1975, 1976 and 1977)
4 Finland
5 Porsche
6 Jaguar (XK)
7 Eric Carlsson
8 Lombard
9 Paddy Hopkirk
10 Finland
11 5 days
12 Jean Pierre Nicolas (France)
13 Skekthar Mehta (Uganda)
14 Vic Elford
15 No one told the local police about the start and the first 58 drivers were all booked for speeding
16 Bath

ROWING

1 Sculling has two oars per man, rowing has one
2 Susan Brown
3 Repêchages
4 Goldie
5 4 miles 374 yards
6 Nottingham
7 Coxed fours, double sculls, coxless pairs, single sculls, coxed pairs, coxless fours, quadruple sculls, eights (the events are always rowed in that order)
8 Chris Baillieu, Michael Hart
9 Anthony Armstrong Jones (Lord Snowdon)
10 50 kilogrammes (7 stone 6 pounds)

Picture Quiz

1 Henley (Royal Regatta)
2 Grand Challenge Cup
3 Diamond Sculls
4 Thames Tradesmen
5 Leander–Thames Tradesmen

RUGBY LEAGUE

A Mixed Bag

1 John Atkinson
2 Dewsbury
3 Hunslet
4 Phil Hogan
5 Billy Boston
6 Syd Hines
7 Leigh
8 Tony Karalius

9 Dewsbury
10 Leeds
11 Keith Elwell
12 Mike Stevenson
13 George Fairburn
14 Leeds Road, Huddersfield

Where Do They Play?

1 (d)
2 (c)
3 (f)
4 (i)
5 (a)
6 (j)
7 (e)
8 (g)
9 (b)
10 (h)

Lance Todd Winners

1 Hull KR
2 Leigh
3 Warrington
4 Widnes
5 Castleford
6 St Helens

Nicknames

1 (c)
2 (j)
3 (h)
4 (a)
5 (i)
6 (b)
7 (e)
8 (f)
9 (g)
10 (d)

Picture Quiz 1

1 Warrington
2 St Helens (20–5)
3 Kel Coslett
4 Wakefield Trinity (12–3)
5 Seven (including two in 1982)

The Challenge Cup

1 St Helens
2 Swinton Park Rangers
3 Wigan
4 Cyril Kellett
5 Mike Smith (Hull)
6 Gus Risman (Workington)
7 Kippax White Swan
8 Leigh and Castleford
9 Halifax, Widnes, Barrow
10 Pilkington Recs

Picture Quiz 2

1 Odsal, Bradford
2 102,575
3 1954, Challenge Cup Final replay
4 Warrington beat Halifax 8–4

The Premiership Trophy

1 St Helens
2 Swinton
3 Kevin Dick (Leeds v. Bradford N)
4 Leeds
5 Geoff Pimblett (St Helens)

RUGBY UNION

Picture Quiz 1

1 Cardiff
2 53
3 20
4 J. P. R. Williams
5 Brynmor Williams

Cap That: Postwar Internationals

1 Leicester
2 J. P. R. Williams
3 Andy Irvine
4 Bob Hiller
5 Billy Beaumont
6 Heriots Former Pupils
7 Northampton
8 Mike Gibson
9 C. P. Meads
10 Tom Kiernan

Picture Quiz 2

(a) Joe Karam
(b) Alan Sutherland

A Mixed Bag

1 John Pullin
2 49 years (1959)
3 Tom Kiernan
4 John Horton
5 Beziers
6 Tony Bond
7 Billy Beaumont
8 Penarth
9 Mike Biggar
10 Warwickshire (1963/64/65)
11 Phil Bennett
12 Dusty Hare
13 Bristol
14 Alan Old
15 Bective Rangers

The Club Tournaments

1 Malcolm Young
2 Bob Mordell
3 Llanelli
4 Blackheath
5 Moseley
6 Heriots FP
7 Moseley
8 Gloucester
9 Cardiff
10 Gala

Picture Quiz 3

1 (a) Mike Lampkowski
   (b) Mark Keyworth
2 Lampkowski, Headingley;
   Keyworth, Swansea
3 Lampkowski went to
   Wakefield Trinity

Picture Quiz 4

1 Ian McLauchlan
2 'Mighty Mouse'
3 Jordanhill
4 Gordon Brown
5 1971 and 1974

Picture Quiz 5

From left: *Back row* – Mike
Knill, Steve Fenwick, Graham
Price, Trevor Evans, Allan
Martin, Charlie Faulkner, Terry
Cobner and Bobby Windsor.
Front row – Gerald Davies,
J.P.R. Williams, Gareth
Edwards, Mervyn Davies, Phil
Bennett, J.J. Williams, and Ray
Gravell

Remember That?

1 Ellis Park, Johannesburg
2 Keith Jarrett
3 Lancashire
4 Munster
5 Norman Sanson
6 Northern
7 Orrell
8 Alistair Hignell
9 Colin Meads
10 Colombes
11 Harlequins
12 The Barbarians
13 Tony Ward
14 Taranaki
15 Australia

SHOOTING

A Mixed Bag

1 Free pistol, small bore rifle
   (prone), small bore rifle
   (three positions), rapid-fire
   pistol, trap shoot, skeet
   shoot, running-game target
2 Bob Braithwaite
3 Lord Swansea
4 10
5 Trap Shooting
6 200
7 25 metres
8 Biathlon
9 Because he said that he
   imagined he was firing
   against his North Korean
   enemies rather than
   targets!

Shooting with a Difference

1 John Wayne
2 *Butch Cassidy and the
   Sundance Kid*
3 *Bonnie and Clyde*
4 *Midnight Cowboy*
5 George C. Scott

SHOW JUMPING

Nationalities

1 West German
2 Welsh
3 American
4 Italian
5 Brazilian
6 Irish

Mix and Match 1

1 (c)
2 (a)
3 (d)
4 (e)
5 (b)
6 (g)
7 (f)

Mix and Match 2

1 (c)
2 (d)
3 (e)
4 (b)
5 (g)
6 (a)
7 (f)

Picture Quiz

1 (a) David Broome on
   Sportsman
   (b) Caroline Bradley on Tigre
2 1972
3 1980
4 1960
5 Marius

SKIING

1 Ingemar Stenmark
2 Jean Claude Killy
3 Andreas and Hanni Wenzel
4 Liechtenstein
5 Toni Sailler (1955–58)
6 Leonhard Stock

Picture Quiz

Gina Hathorn

SKI JUMPING

1 Two
2 70 metres
3 1964
4 0.5 metres
5 20
6 Karl Schnabel
7 The in run (the landing area is known as the out run)
8 Garmisch, Bischofshofen, Oberstorf, and Innsbruck
9 Bischofshofen
10 Czechoslovakian

Picture Quiz

Toni Innauer:
Austria; 70-metre hill
Jouko Tormanen:
Finland; 90-metre hill

SNOOKER

The Davis Connection

1 Chesterfield
2 OBE
3 Barry Hearn
4 UK Professional Championship
5 Once (in 1940, Joe won 37–36)
6 Walter Donaldson
7 John Spencer and David Taylor

Picture Quiz 1

1 *From left*: Ed Stewart, Fred Trueman, Frankie Vaughan, Kenny Lynch, Arthur Mullard, John H. Stracey, Alex Higgins, Rex Williams, Eddie Charlton, Fred Davis, John Spencer
2 Rex Williams and Fred Davis
3 Eddie Charlton
4 Lance Gibbs
5 Jose Napoles (John H. Stracey)

Picture Quiz 2

1 Six, between 1970 and 1978
2 One, in 1982
3 John Spencer (1971 and 1977)

Pot Luck

1 Crucible Theatre, Sheffield
2 Tony Knowles
3 Ray Reardon
4 Kirk Stevens
5 Patsy Fagan
6 John Spencer (1977)
7 John Spencer (1972), Ray Reardon (1982)
8 Cliff Thorburn
9 Jimmy White
10 Dennis Taylor

SOFTBALL

1 Baseball
2 Nine
3 USA
4 Three
5 60 feet
6 Seven
7 In softball the pitching is underarm
8 A softball is bigger and heavier than a baseball. It consists of a cork and rubber (or Kapok) centre enclosed by yarn and covered in latex or leather
9 Kitten ball or mush ball
10 Australia (Melbourne)

SPEED SKATING

1 Eric Heiden (USA)
2 Dutch
3 10,000 metres
4 Norway
5 Two
6 500 metres, 1500 metres, 5000 metres, 10,000 metres
7 Sheila Young (1976) and Beth Heiden (1980)

Picture Quiz

500 metres: Karin Enke (East Germany)
1500 metres: Annie Borcink (Holland)
3000 metres: Eva Jensen (Norway)

SPEEDWAY

The Foreign Connection
1 New Zealander
2 Danish
3 Swedish
4 Swedish
5 New Zealander
6 English
7 Australian
8 New Zealander
9 American
10 Welsh

A Mixed Bag
1 Hackney (1980)
2 White City
3 Bobby Schwartz
4 Malcolm Simmons
5 New Zealand
6 Belle Vue, 1970, 1971, 1972
7 Ole Olsen (Denmark), 1978
8 Dave Lanning
9 Ronnie Moore (1954)
10 Jerzy Szczakiel

Home Ground
1 White City
2 Wolverhampton
3 Halifax
4 Birmingham (National Exhibition Centre)
5 Ipswich
6 Swindon
7 Wembley
8 Cradley Heath

Which Club Did They Ride For?
1 Leicester
2 New Cross
3 Belle Vue
4 Wembley
5 Cradley Heath
6 Halifax
7 Newcastle
8 King's Lynn

SQUASH

1 Ireland
2 Harrow
3 Heather McKay
4 21 feet
5 Geoff Hunt (Australia)
6 9 feet
7 9
8 Four
9 Vicki Cardwell (Hoffman) of Australia

Picture Quiz
1 Geoff Hunt holding the cup, and in the match, Qamar Zaman (left) playing Jonah Barrington
2 Hunt, eight; Barrington, six; Zaman, one
3 Hunt, 1969, 1974, 1976, 1977, 1978, 1979, 1980, 1981; Barrington, 1967, 1968, 1970, 1971, 1972, 1973; Zaman, 1975
4 Churchill Theatre, Bromley
5 20 (1962–82)

SWIMMING & DIVING

Picture Quiz
1 (a) Brian Brinkley
  (b) Shane Gould
  (c) Mark Spitz
  (d) David Wilkie
2 12: Spitz, 9; Gould, 2; Wilkie, 1; Brinkley, 0
3 1972
4 Seven (1976)
5 Three – one gold (1976), two silvers (1972–76)

British Olympic Medallists
1 Martyn Woodruffe
2 Lucy Morton (1924, 200 m breaststroke)
3 Margaret Edwards
4 Liz Ferris
5 Bobby McGregor
6 Helen Jameson
7 Natalie Steward
8 Henry Taylor (1908, 400 m freestyle and 1500 m freestyle)
9 Phillip Hubble
10 Cathy Gibson

A Mixed Bag
1 Duncan Goodhew
2 Johnny Weissmuller
3 Anita Lonsborough
4 Brian Phelps
5 Nine (seven in 1972, two in 1968)
6 Dawn Fraser (Australia)
7 Beckenham
8 South African
9 Backstroke (100 and 200 metres)
10 David Wilkie

Who . . . ?
1 Jackie Wilmott (silver in 800-metres freestyle)
2 Sharron Davies
3 Robertas Zulpa (USSR)
4 Michelle Ford (Australia), 800-metres freestyle
5 Victor Davis (Canada)
6 Jim Montgomery (USA), 49.99 seconds in 1976

TEN-PIN BOWLING

1 300
2 60 feet
3 Pauline Smith (London)
4 A turkey
5 Knocking all ten pins down with two balls
6 Richard Nixon
7 16 pounds
8 Gutters
9 15 inches
10 34

TRAMPOLINE

1 USA
2 Paul Luxon
3 15 feet
4 Synchronized trampolining
5 Every two years
6 10
7 Four
8 Stewart Matthews
9 Judy Wills (USA)

WATER POLO

1 1 metre
2 3 metres (9 feet 10¼ inches)
3 Referee, two timekeepers, two secretaries, two goal judges
4 5 minutes
5 Seven
6 Manchester (Manchester Osborne)
7 It was the first ever international, between England and Scotland
8 Hungary
9 United States
10 Italy (the host nation)

WATER SKIING

1 Mike Hazelwood and Andy Mapple
2 Mike Hazelwood
3 Karen Morse
4 75 feet
5 United States (in 1922, when Ralph Samuelson first used water skis)
6 Esther Williams
7 Scarborough
8 Slalom, jumping, figures, ski racing, long-distance skiing, tricks

YACHTING

1 *Gypsy Moth III*
2 Eric Tabarlay
3 The America's Cup
4 Star, Soling, Tempest, Dragon
5 The America's Cup
6 *Freedom*
7 King Constantine of Greece
8 Ireland (Royal Cork Yacht Club)
9 K
10 Acapulco

Picture Quiz

1 1972
2 Kiel, West Germany
3 Chris Davies
4 Iain McDonald-Smith
5 Flying Dutchman

YOU NAME IT

Amateur and Professional Wrestling

1 You are not allowed to seize the opponent below the hips in Greco-Roman
2 Ken Richmond

Professional Wrestling

1 (c)
2 (e)
3 (f)
4 (b)
5 (d)
6 (a)

American Football

1 (e)
2 (d)
3 (a)
4 (c)
5 (b)

Baseball

1 (d)
2 (f)
3 (g)
4 (a)
5 (b)
6 (c)
7 (e)

Basketball

1 Team Fiat
2 Hemel Hempstead
3 Solent All Stars
4 Crystal Palace
5 Alton Byrd
6 Birchwood
7 Crystal Palace

Cross-Country Running

1 John Treacy
2 Longchamps
3 Norwegian
4 David Bedford
5 Gaston Roelents
6 Rumania (women's title, 1978)
7 New Zealand (1975)
8 Mohammed Gammoudi (Tunisia)
9 Craig Virgin, 1980–81

Cycling Picture Quiz

1 Scarborough
2 1971
3 Fedor Den Hertog
4 Les West

Cycling
The Tour de France

1 Jan Janssen (1968)
2 Shay Elliott
3 Freddie Maertens (Belgium)
4 Plymouth
5 Bernard Thevenet
6 Brian Robinson
7 Louison Bobet
8 Jacques Anquetil and Eddie Merckx
9 Switzerland
10 Barry Hoban (now married to Simpson's wife)

Odds 'n' Ends

1 Frisbee golf
2 The training of horses
3 You sit on a luge; you lie on a toboggan
4 Soup
5 Speed skating, figure skating, dancing

6 440 yards
7 Draw shot
8 Graham Noyce
9 Swiss
10 Trotting
11 Kevin Keegan
12 Laurie McMenemy (Southampton manager)
13 Racing abandoned – no wind
14 He was disqualified for infringing rules!
15 Fred Trueman
16 Brian Barnes
17 Hugh McIlvanney (*Observer*)

Sums

1 26 (11 + 15)
2 11 (7 + 4)
3 13 (6 + 7)
4 30 (18 + 12)
5 21 (6 + 15)

Table Tennis

1 Swaythling Cup (men); Corbillon Cup (women)
2 John Hilton
3 Victor Barna
4 Johnny Leach
5 Ann Jones (then Haydon)

Three-Day Eventing

1 Doublet
2 Goodwill
3 Jane Bullen
4 George, Killaire, Be Fair, Wideawake
5 Richard Meade or Hugh Thomas
6 Mark Phillips
7 Warrior

Weightlifting

1 The Snatch and the Clean and Jerk
2 New Zealand
3 Vasili Alexeev

Picture Quiz

1 Vassili Alexeyev (USSR)
2 1972 and 1976
3 Cooking!
4 Sultan Rakhmanov (USSR)
5 Over 110 kilos

Would You Believe It?

1 Reginald Bosanquet
2 A beard
3 Jim Reeves
4 World Steamroller Championships
5 Bob Seagren (pole vaulter)
6 He went off for his tea at 4 p.m., as he always has his tea at 4 on Sundays – like the Queen
7 Lingfield Park
8 John Stonehouse or Ian Brady
9 World Pea-Shooting Championship
10 Jerry Pate
11 The plane on which their opponents were travelling was hijacked and they spent the afternoon in Nicosia Airport
12 Underwater hockey!
13 They both holed in one on the same day at the same hole in the same match at Sidmouth Golf Club
14 Boxing – he's the Scottish ABA Light Heavyweight Champion
15 Seven
16 He got married